Was It Meant To Be?

Debbie Dennis was born in Wandsworth, London in 1966, a 'World Cup Baby'.

When she was growing up her father worked as a dustman in Brixton, and would sometimes take her out on the truck with him, which she very much enjoyed.

She has an older sister and a younger brother with whom she shared a happy childhood, they especially enjoyed their teenage years in the 1980s and shared a passion for the music of that era in particular; Wham, Culture Club and Madonna. Debbie met her first love in the 1980s also, which brings back very fond memories.

Debbie has a good bond with her mother, who has helped her extensively over the years.

Was It Meant To Be?

Debbie Dennis

Was It Meant To Be?

Olympia Publishers
London

First Published in 2013

Olympia Publishers
60 Cannon Street
London
EC4N 6NP

Printed in Great Britain

For Timothy, my husband, who has inspired me.

Acknowledgements

To all my friends and family that have been there for me and kept me sane, no matter what; I love you all.

Contents

Chapter 1

Summer loving

It was a warm summer evening in 1981. Anita, a slim, short haired blonde and blue eyed girl was standing outside the youth club with friends while they were having crafty cigarettes. Someone poked Anita in the back saying 'Anita, Anita.'

Anita turned around to see who it was and saw that it was Darren and Neil, twins, slim build, brown hair, short from school, saying 'Our mate Mark fancies you, will you go out with him?' Anita looked across to see a tall, good looking skinhead, wearing rolled up jeans, Dr Marten boots and a blue, checked shirt, staring at her with his big blue eyes and a cheeky grin on his face.

Anita found herself saying, whilst a little lost for words, 'Yeah, yes, ok.' As Darren and Neil went over to tell Mark, Anita ran back inside with Carol, 5ft, green eyes, dark haired, slim build and Mags, tall, dark skinned and slim.

Anita sat at the table having a Coke with the girls, Mark came over with Darren and Neil and joined them, so Anita moved over to let Mark sit next to her. In the, background *'Being with you,'* by Smokey Robinson was playing in the disco hall. Anita and Mark found themselves talking all evening, even when their friends went off into the disco. Mark told Anita he was from the Isle of Wight, and that his parents had split up and his mum had moved nearby with him, his brothers James, Gordy and his sister Sheila, and that he went to Anita's school.

When the disco ended and it was time to leave, Carol and Mags, who lived a couple of doors away from Anita, always walked back together. Mark said 'Can I walk you home?'

To which Anita replied 'Yes.' So all 6 of them set off home. As they neared Anita's house, Mark grabbed her by her hand and pulled her up close to him and kissed her goodnight so tenderly, Anita's heart skipped a beat.

At school the next day Anita, sitting with Carol and Mags on the field, saw Mark and Neil walking towards them. Mark and Anita sat holding hands and cuddling, and when they went back in for lessons, kissed in the corridors.

Anita and her sister Diane just under 5 foot, slim build with shoulder length blonde hair, were listening to music with Carol, getting ready to go out with Mark and his friends. Mum, a 5 foot lady, slim build and brown hair, was waiting around with them whilst they were giggling and spraying lots of hairspray around trying to get their hair flicks just perfect. Then there was a knock on the door, Anita ran to answer it.

Mark stood there with Darren and Neil and another two of his friends who were brothers, Roy and Paul, both around 5 foot 5 with blonde hair and full of themselves. Anita was just about to let them in when Dad, a stern 6 foot man, came down the stairs, took one look at Mark and said to Anita, 'He's not coming in here.'

Anita asked 'Why?'

Dad immediately looked at Mark and said to Mark [whilst pointing at Mark's badge] 'That's why, no-one is coming in my house with a Nazi badge on.' Mark apologised to dad and took the badge off. Mark and his friends waited outside.

Anita, Diane and Carol joined them shortly, with Anita slightly embarrassed about Dad's behaviour. Mark had told her not to worry and that he thought her dad was scary.

Anita and Carol started going to the scout hut disco as Mark and his friends went there to listen to Ska music, with a lot of music by groups such as Bad Manners, The Specials, Selector and The Beat were played. Mark always walked Anita back home and kissed her goodnight.

'Anita,' shouted Carol 'come look at this,' and dragged her down the school corridor to a commotion that was going on. It was Mark and his friends; they had set off the fire extinguishers and were soaking everyone going by. Anita and Carol giggled at this. Next thing, the head master was marching up behind them ordering Mark and his friends to his office immediately. Nevertheless, Mark was put on detention and was ordered to clean up the biology lab after school. Mark had the devil in him that day and when he was left alone in the lab and noticed that he had to clean up the bull's eyes that had been examined that day, Mark decided to take the bag of bull's eyes home with him for a laugh. His friends had already left as they were all given separate chores to do. Walking to the bus stop outside school, Mark saw there was a girl already waiting at the bus stop. Mark didn't know her name. All of a sudden Mark had an urge to empty the bull's eyes over the girl's head, leaving her screaming hysterically and she ran back into school. Mark thought that this was hilarious and laughed to himself nearly all the way home.

After having his tea at home and a bath, Mark set off to Anita's house. Anita was already outside with Carol and some of her other friends, Tanzi, a tall blonde haired and blue eyed girl, and Mags and were just chatting. Mark told them what he had done at school, and they told him that it was disgusting, although initially they all laughed about it. Darren and Neil came along and another of Mark's friends, Arnie, so they all decided to just walk around and chat and ended up sitting in the park as it was a warm evening, until it was time to go home.

The next day at school Mark once again was called into the headmaster's office and was suspended for the rest of term.

The school summer holidays were upon them and Anita was going to stay at her aunt's in Canada, with her sister Diane, and although looking forward to the holiday she didn't want to leave Mark for so long. As they said their goodbyes the night before, tears rolled down Anita's face and they kissed and cuddled and held on to each other for what seemed like forever.

On arrival at the airport in Canada, aunt Floss, 5 foot, slim build, and uncle Bob a 6 foot 2, slim man, with Anita and Diane's cousins, Tracy, long brown hair 5ft and slim, Derek, a cheeky 5 year old, and baby Katy were waiting to greet them. They flung their arms around each other as they had not seen each other for about eighteen months when they immigrated to Canada. It was so nice to see them and to be spending the school holidays there was going to be great.

The next morning Anita, Diane and Tracy set off to the shopping mall to meet Tracy's friends. They all had a great day and were exhausted by the time they arrived back at auntie Floss's apartment, the smell of roast lamb cooking in the oven. Auntie Floss was a great cook and did the best cauliflower cheese in the world.

After dinner Anita told them all about Mark and how she was going to miss him and wanted to buy a present to take back home for him, so Auntie Floss said she would take Anita shopping before they went back home to England.

The next morning they were all up early, Auntie Floss and Uncle Bob had a surprise for them. They were all going camping in the Rocky Mountains, 'Wow, how great was this going to be.' When they arrived at the camp site, Auntie Floss's friends were there with their children and in the evening all the adults went to the pub, leaving the teenagers on site.

Anita, Diane and Tracy were all in the tent when they heard what they thought were bears growling and prowling around outside. All three of them were too scared to go out and look and eventually fell asleep. The next morning they found out it was some lads messing around. That morning they got up early and went shopping in Banff and they really did see some bears across the road, climbing in the bins. The rangers were soon there to move the bears on. The views in the mountains were absolutely beautiful.

That afternoon, they drove to Lake Louise, it was the most beautiful lake Anita had ever seen, so blue and just glistening in the sunlight. Anita felt like she could sit there forever in the sun. Just then, Derek ran up behind her, he was ten years younger than Anita and liked to tease the girls. Anita chased Derek around the lake just laughing and playing around and tickled him when she caught him. After a couple of days they went back home to the apartment.

Anita, Diane and Tracy spent most of their days in Edmonton mall with friends or around friends' houses, just having a laugh. It was coming up for the end of July and nearly Anita's fifteenth birthday and also Aunt Floss and Uncle Bob's wedding anniversary which happened to be the same day. Anita, Diane and Tracy decided to go buy Aunt Floss and Uncle Bob a surprise anniversary cake and had fun choosing it, they arranged to collect it the morning of Anita's birthday. Anita carried on looking around the shops whilst Tracy and Diane decided to surprise Anita with a birthday cake. When they returned home to the smell of Aunt Floss's cooking, they all giggled to themselves about the surprises.

The morning of Anita's birthday, the telephone was ringing, it was Mum and Dad to wish Anita a happy birthday and Aunt Floss and Uncle Bob a happy anniversary. Anita spoke to her brother, Tom, before he went out with his friends. Tom was only eighteen months younger than Anita and was into everything, being cheeky with his friends. After the telephone call, the girls got ready and went to the mall to collect the cakes. Anita was amazed and happy that they had brought her a cake too and returned home just after lunch to Uncle Bob telling them that they were all going out for dinner that evening to The Spaghetti Factory, every meal contained pasta of some sort, they all tucked in, enjoying their meals and alcohol free cocktails which they thought were brilliant. When they returned home that night, the girls sat up listening to the radio and decided to ring in requests as the station was asking for them. They chatted to the DJ live on air and were all giggly. After they got bored with this they decided to watch television till late, as they were determined to have a late night, it was now 3 o'clock in the morning and, flicking the channels, they watched Charles and Diana getting married as it was later back home in England. After watching the wedding they were all feeling very tired and went to bed.

Anita was so relaxed and having a great time although missing Mark terribly, she found herself writing a lot of poetry and reading it out whilst sitting on the toilet, to everyone's amusement. One day the girls went swimming in the pool attached to the apartments. Diane was swimming along with Tracy when lots of lads came in for a swim. Anita was sitting on the side paddling and noticed Diane's bikini top had fallen down. She found this really funny and without thinking shouted out in front of everyone 'Di, your tits are hanging out.' Diane nearly died of embarrassment at Anita's remark. Diane didn't speak to Anita for a couple of days. Anita was not bothered; she found great pleasure in getting her sister, even though she couldn't specifically remember what for.

A week had passed and it was going to be Diane's sixteenth birthday in a couple of days. Diane was speaking to Anita again now, the girls all went to the mall shopping. Tracy and Anita got Diane a birthday cake and they went and had lunch in the mall, chips and gravy. 'Wow how delicious is this,' Anita said, as she had never tasted anything like this before. When they returned, Aunt Floss and Uncle Bob had a surprise for them, they had their friends around and all had a barbeque party to celebrate Diane's birthday. It was a really good evening and the girls were tired by the end of it.

That night, when they went to bed, Anita decided to tell them a ghost story, just off her head. She managed to frighten Tracy and Diane and herself so much, none of them wanted to go to sleep without the light on, although eventually they went to sleep. The next day, Aunt Floss and Uncle Bob had gone to work and all three girls were in charge of baby Katy. Derek had gone to his friend's for the day. Anita thought it would be funny to jump out on Katy at every opportunity, frightening the life out of her, after a while Katy got used to it and thought it was funny, so Anita was running around playing with Katy all day.

It was now the end of August and it would be time to go home in a couple of days. So Aunt Floss took Anita shopping to buy a present for Mark. Anita bought Mark a silver St. Christopher on a chain and was pleased with herself. At the airport, ready to fly home, they said their goodbyes. Anita cried, hugging Uncle Bob and Aunt Floss, she was going to miss them and her cousins so much. She had such a great time with them.

Chapter 2

Halloween

Arriving home, Anita could not wait to see Mark, wanting to see him that day to give him his present. Mark was so happy to see Anita, he told her his brother Gordy had left home after a row and didn't know where he was. Then they just kissed and cuddled until Mark went home.

The next day Mark came round early before lunch time, he said he had a row with his mum and needed to get out of the house. Dad was already preparing Sunday dinner as he had bought a great big leg of lamb. Dad asked Mark if he would like to stay for dinner. Mark said that he would, so Dad told Mark to go check with his mum first. Mark said his mum never cooked a Sunday roast whether they were in or not and he would normally do himself something when he got home. Dad appeared to soften towards Mark when he got this reply. Mum then came into the kitchen and soon took over as Dad was taking Tom out to his friend's. Mum got Mark involved in helping her cook the dinner and showing him what to do. After dinner was in the oven cooking, and too soon for the veggies, Anita and Mark went for a walk just round and about returning home in time to help Mum with the rest of the cooking as Mark seemed so interested. When dinner was ready everyone sat at the table chatting whilst having dinner. Anita was really happy that Mum and Dad let Mark join them. After dinner, Mark thanked Mum and Dad, Anita and Mark washed up, then joined the rest of the family watching television for the evening.

Back at school, Anita and Mark were always together during break with their friends. One day the school deputy stopped them and told them off for kissing in the corridors, they didn't take any notice and just carried on. One weekend, cousins Frank and Benny were coming to stay. Anita got on well with them, but they just lived so far away, so would now and again spend weekends with them. Mark and Anita were out with Frank and Mark's friends Paul and Roy. Mark and Anita were always holding hands and kissing and cuddling and their friends told them to just go get a room. As they were walking past a block of flats, they went into the building to sit on the stairs as it was chilly outside. Mark noticed an empty cupboard and got up holding Anita's hand. Frank, Roy and Paul were still sitting on the stairs chatting. Mark and Anita went into the cupboard and shut the door. It was really dark inside there. Mark started kissing Anita and put his hand inside her top feeling her breasts, so gently, then got Anita's hand and said 'Come on babe, just stop if you want to,' then put Anita's hand down his jeans to where he had an erection. He rubbed Anita's hand on his penis and ejaculated over the top of his jeans and over Anita's foot. They carried on kissing for a while before coming out, both feeling a little embarrassed when they emerged. Frank, Roy and Paul cheered and asked what they did, though Anita and Mark just left it to their imaginations.

The next day Frank, Anita and Mark decided to go to the cinema, they got the bus into Croydon and arrived at the cinema. Frank and Mark wanted to see an eighteen rated film, so Anita just went along with it. As they got to the box office, the manager questioned Anita's age, so she could not get in. Frank and Mark were ok, they got away with it being tall, so none of them could see the film, as they were not going in without Anita. They all ended up going for a burger instead, before returning home.

Uncle Sava arrived the following day to take Frank and Benny home. He had to wait for Benny to return with Tom as he was playing with Tom and his friends. Mum asked them to stop for tea before returning home and invited Mark for tea as well. Mark was interested in making the tea with Mum and so helped.

After tea they said their goodbyes, as Uncle Sava had a long drive back home. As they left, Mark and Anita sat in and watched the television, snuggled up together as it was chilly outside, they were just so consumed in themselves they didn't always notice anyone else around them. A knock on the door and Dad shouted Anita. It was her friend Tia. Tia had a slim build and in height was the same as Anita, but with long blonde hair, lots of friends called her Blondie. Tia needed to talk to Anita without everyone listening. Tia told Anita that she was pregnant and couldn't believe it and whatever happened she was going to keep her baby. Anita was shocked to hear this but, although shocked, was there, and always would be for her friend. Tia then left as she had a friend waiting for her and said she would see Anita in a couple of days. Anita went back into the living room and told her family, who also appeared to be shocked at the news. Anita then snuggled back up to Mark.

It was the weekend, Anita went round to Mark's house. James answered the door saying 'Mark's having a dump you better come in and wait for him, come up and play the Atari with me.' So Anita followed James upstairs and saw that James was joking, as Mark was playing on the Atari already with James.

James said to Anita 'Eugh you kiss my brother, that's gross.' Anita just laughed. They all spent the afternoon playing the Atari. Mark's Mum came in to see what they were all up to bringing them some sausage rolls and then went back downstairs leaving them to it.

It was Halloween night, and Mark and Anita went out with Roy, Paul, Carol and Mags and sat on the wall outside the woods. Mark and Anita went into the woods, leaving their friends outside. They found a secluded area. Mark took off his Crombie coat and laid it on the ground. It was cold outside and fireworks could be heard. Nervously Mark started kissing Anita, caressing her, and made love to Anita in the woods. Both losing their virginity together at the age of fifteen. They lay there cuddling for a while before going back outside to their friends, who immediately guessed what they had done and cheered at the red faced couple. Anita told Carol about it before going home and as usual Mark kissed Anita goodnight before going home.

Somehow Anita's mum guessed and just asked 'Are you sleeping with Mark?'
'Yes,' replied Anita. Next thing their parents arranged a meeting with the two of them, discussing if they would allow them to sleep together as they were both under age. Mark's mum stood up for them and said 'If they are going to do it, they will do it wherever and I'd rather them be safe, and they can be here.'

Anita's dad said 'No way is that happening under my roof.' Consequently Anita stayed over at Mark's house a lot. Mark's mum converted her laundry room into a bedroom for Mark as he had previously shared a room with his brother James. Anita and Mark were inseparable, going everywhere together. One evening after school, whilst out with their friends, they sneaked into the infant school field through a hole in the fence. Anita and Mark ran down into the playground and went and sat in the tunnel and made love in the tunnel. As Mark sat up, still with his pants down, he sat on an ant's nest and got his bum bitten, which was hilariously funny to their friends for a long time.

At every opportunity Mark and Anita got the house to themselves, if at Anita's house they would go up to the bedroom and make love as many times as they could before any one came home, sometimes having to get up quickly and get dressed if they heard the front door going, in case it was a parent coming home.

Mum and Dad told Anita that they were thinking of going out for an Indian meal at a restaurant that they used regularly and asked Anita to ask Mark if he wanted to come with them and they would treat him. As Mark arrived at Anita's that day, she asked him straight away. Mark was a bit worried at this as he never had an Indian before. Anita told him it's fine and that he would love it.

As they arrived at the restaurant that evening, the waiter brought them all poppadums and dips while they waited for their meals. Dad had Mark trying a bit of everything and Mark enjoyed it. 'Told you,' said Anita smiling. Mark and Anita were getting more and more inseparable and appeared to spend every free moment with each other. They regularly saw their friends with each other and went to see Tia regularly to see how she was getting on in her pregnancy. Tia was now sixteen, she was a few months older than Anita and they just happened to be in the same school year together. Anita did worry about her friend, Tia seemed ok though.

At a family meal one evening with Anita's family, Anita's cousin Pete said to Anita 'Why don't you two go your separate ways and if it's meant to be, you will find each other again somehow.'

Anita was horrified at even the thought of being without Mark for a day let alone a lifetime, and told Pete 'I don't ever want to be without Mark, I love him so much.'

Pete just laughed and said 'Don't go rushing into things, you are too young'.

After Christmas, in the January of 1982, Anita had pains in her side walking home from school with Mark, so popped in to see the doctor, who said it was Anita's appendix and arranged for a ambulance to take her to hospital that evening. The next morning, coming round after her operation, Mark was waiting for her to wake up; Darren and Neil were with him. They told Anita to listen to the radio as Mark had asked for her favourite song at the time to be played for her. It was 'Don't you want me' by Human League. Mark stayed until visiting time was over and continued to visit every day until Anita was back home at the weekend. Anita's dad was cooking lamb roast and Mark stayed for dinner as he did most Sundays now, Anita had to stay in and could not go back to school until she had recovered.

Anita and Mark sat in the back room, away from the rest of the family so they could be on their own, although still in pain, Anita managed to make love to Mark quietly with everyone else in the house. Mark pulled his trousers up just in time before Anita's dad came in to see if she was ok. That was a close one, they thought as they giggled to themselves.

'Hurry up you two,' shouted Sheila. 'We're going to be late for the show; I'll wait in the car with Daryl.'

'Come on babe, hurry up with your hair,' said Mark.
'I'm coming, I'm coming, don't rush me, got to get my hair right,' Anita replied giggling. Then they both ran out to Sheila and

Daryl, Sheila's boyfriend, to go to the cinema to watch The Rocky Horror Show.

When they arrived, there was a big queue with lots of people dressed in suspenders. It was nothing Anita had experienced before, and holding onto Mark went in with Sheila and Daryl. As they all sat down in their seats, ready to watch the film, the trailers began, and the cinema ushers were lining up around the room, which Anita thought was very strange. As the film started it was raining with hailstones in the film, the ushers squirted water pistols at the people sitting in their seats, then threw rice at them, which had the whole cinema laughing, and when the Time Warp song came on, the ushers got up with some of the audience and danced to it. It was such a great night and such good company with Sheila and Daryl.

Sheila had got a new job with living accommodation and invited Mark and Anita round for dinner. Sheila was a personal assistant to one of her previous salon clients, and was home alone while her boss was away, leaving Sheila to look after the three dogs, Barney, Benji and Bruce. Anita thought brilliant, as she loved dogs and her mum wouldn't let her have one. Anita and Mark helped Sheila to cook the tripe, which stank the kitchen out and then walked the dogs before they settled down to a lovely dinner which Sheila had cooked. Anita and Mark spent a lot of time with Sheila and had a lot of laughs with both her and Daryl.

One day Sheila and Daryl invited Anita and Mark to go to a party with them, so they all went along together that evening. Anita and Mark chatted to different people and one person Anita was chatting to was having a sex change. Wow thought Anita can they really do that, how can that be done she wondered. Some of the people they met that night opened Anita's eyes up to the gay community and she realised then and there, that they are not strange; they are just normal people like you and me, as she told Mark. Although growing up with certain people around calling the gay community 'poofters and freaks', Anita found this to be totally unfounded, and enjoyed their company, and so Anita and Mark went to many more parties taking Carol and her boyfriend Gary and just had fun.

Chapter 3

Isle of Wight

The next summer holidays, after Anita and Mark had both left school, they were due to start training courses in the September, so decided to spend the holidays with Mark's dad on the Isle of Wight.

They got the train to Portsmouth, heading for the ferry port. Mark and Anita sneaked into an empty carriage as the train was quite empty and Anita, wearing a mini rah-rah skirt, straddled Mark and they made love in the carriage, then snuggled up together until the train pulled in at Portsmouth.

Arriving at Portsmouth, Anita and Mark took the ferry to the Isle of Wight, and got off at Ryde, then got the train to Sandown to Mark's dad's house. Mark's dad lived with his girlfriend and her two children, Richie and Lea. After their arrival, they all sat and had dinner together. The next day Lea had a horse show to attend, so Mark and Anita went along to watch the show. Lea won some rosettes for her horse jumps. It was a lovely day and the sun was shining.

That evening Mark took Anita out for dinner, they went to an Indian restaurant and, although they were only both just turned sixteen at the time, had a candle-lit dinner and a bottle of wine, it was a lovely romantic evening. That night, when they got back and were in bed, Anita had a stomach ache and had to run to the toilet, then had diarrhoea all through the night until the next morning. Mark had to wake his dad to find out where he kept the toilet tissue. Anita was so embarrassed; everyone found it amusing the next morning when her stomach had settled.

That day, Mark and Anita headed off to Mark's brother, Arron's and his wife Kimmy's house in Shanklin. They all spent the day on the beach and as it was such a beautiful day they took a picnic. Mark took his top off as it was so hot and to go in the sea, Arron said 'What's that?' as Mark had love bites on his body which he'd forgotten about. Arron jokingly told Anita off. Mark and Anita got in the dinghy and bobbed about in the sea. After a while they realised they were going out a bit too far, and next thing Arron had swum out to them telling them it's dangerous to be out so far, and swam them back to shore.

The next day Mark and Anita hired bicycles to ride around the island and rode away, just stopping for lunch and taking photos on the way. They were riding down some steps to the beach with Anita screaming nearly all the way down. They found a secluded part of the beach and sunbathed for a while before riding around again and wore themselves out. That night they just fell into bed shattered.

Refreshed and full of life, the next morning Mark and Anita set off to Black Gang chine, being silly and running around the chine taking photos of each other in the fairy castle and by the fountain. Anita and Mark just had so much love for each other and never wanted anything to ever get in the way. That evening back at Mark's dad's, they ate cheese toasties while playing pool and Mark's dad told them off for getting crumbs on the table, so they were more careful in future. Mark rang his brother, Shane, to see if he was about to visit him while they were there, but Shane was at work so they were not able to see him before returning home.

On returning back home, Mark and Anita settled into training courses before going to work.

On the weekends, they started going out with Carol and Gary a lot, all 4 of them went to Brighton one day, getting the train from Croydon. Arriving in Brighton, they messed about in the sea and sunbathed, and ran across to the chippy for lunch followed by ice-cream. Mark and Anita also went out to discos and the pub with Carol and Gary a lot. One day they got the tube into London going to Camden town, as they often went to the markets. Unknown to them there was an IRA bomb alert, London was in a panic, but the friends were all oblivious to this, and only found out when they got home to panicking parents, not knowing if they were ok.

At Mark's house one morning, watching TV with mum and Pops, Mark's stepfather, Mark and Anita were bored so decided to go to Crystal Palace park for the day and take brother James. They invited their friend Tracey who'd had the baby already and was living on her own now. Tracey couldn't make it as the baby wasn't well. They took a picnic and went to the zoo but unfortunately forgot their camera, they usually took photos everywhere they went. On return they walked the dog, Mark and Anita stayed at Mark's house for a couple of days to have time to themselves, without their friends for a change.

A few months later Mark's, mum and Pops decided to move away. Mark did not want to go with them, as he did not want to move away from Anita. After lots of searching for flats, Mark finally moved into a hostel flat next to Crystal Palace football ground. Mark learnt a lot from this, having to cook and clean his flat. Most days Anita came and cooked for both of them. Not long after, another lad called Wayne moved in, Mark and Wayne became good friends.

Mark and Anita enjoyed buying bits for the flat as it helped them build up things for when they moved in together. They bought a red and white dinner service and an ironing board, as well as many other things.

Mark became ill with a bad chest infection, which turned into bronchitis and he ended up in hospital for days. Anita went to visit every day after working, till visiting time was over, getting the bus back home on her own late at night. Mark was soon on the mend but started getting blackouts and was diagnosed with epilepsy. Although it didn't really affect Mark, apart from the shakes, which Mark had since Anita had known him, although obviously not knowing the cause at the time.

Anita had just got home from Mark's and dad told her he thought she was spending too much time at Mark's and that she looked worn out. Anita and dad started rowing and Anita would not back down especially when she found out that mum and dad had let Diane's boyfriend move in. Anita went out of control, screaming at them, all the time Mark needed somewhere and she helped Mark look everywhere for a place to live. Diane's boyfriend has a row with his father and moves into their home. It's just not right thought Anita. Cousin Pete was on the phone later that evening and Dad told Pete that Anita had gone mental and out of control. Pete asked to speak to Anita who was very emotional at this point and Pete asked Anita to come and move in with him and his family for a while and came and picked Anita up. Anita loved being at Pete's and got on well with his wife and the children. Mark got on well with them too.

A few months went by and Anita moved back home. She loved being at Pete's but thought that his family needed their space and didn't really need her there but still went and babysat for Pete when he went out.

Chapter 4
Where did it all go wrong?

One day, Mark and Anita went to visit Aunt Rae, They began to visit her quite a lot, they loved being in her company and felt very welcome. Rae had two girls, Anita's cousins, Bex and Mo. Anita and Mark would take them out in their prams, pretending that they were their own children. Not long after this, Mark asked Anita to have a baby with him. Anita refused, telling Mark that she was too young to be having children and they should enjoy their lives and have children in a few years, although she loved Mark very much. Anita wanted to get married and have a career before thinking about babies. Mark appeared upset at this but he loved Anita so much and listened to what she was saying, after all it made sense; they were far too young to be having babies.

Visiting Anita's nan one day, nan asked Mark and Anita if they would look after her house whilst her and granddad went on a holiday for 3 weeks, they said yes to this straight away. It was like having a holiday. Mark and Anita didn't have showers at home and nan had a shower, so Mark and Anita took every chance they could to make love in the shower and made the most of having the house to themselves, by this time they were both seventeen and working out what they wanted in life.

It was now April 1984, Anita's friend Cassie told Anita that she had a dream that Anita dies in a car crash and it was so real that it frightened Cassie. That evening they were all due to go to Carol's eighteenth birthday party, so they all got ready and went to the party and had a great evening. Carol looking beautiful as ever, and glowing on her birthday. On the way home, they could not all fit in the same car. Cassie begged Anita not to get in a different car to her but they could not all fit in and Anita and Mark wanted to be together so got in another car which was the car in front of the one that Cassie was in. The drivers had both been drinking and decided to race. The car that Mark and Anita were in hit the bend and flipped over, knocking Anita out, everyone was in shock. Cassie in the car behind saw it happen just like in her dream and screamed hysterically.

Mark smashed the rest of the back window open and pulled Anita out of the car and laid her on the bank. Anita came round and had to slap Cassie as she was hysterical and did not notice that Anita was alive. This put Anita off getting into a car for a long time and she would only get the bus for a while.

Anita and Cassie started spending a lot of time together along with Mark with them both. Cassie asked Anita to move in with her as she had been offered a flat in New Addington in Croydon. Anita moved in with Cassie and loved having her independence, although Anita loved Mark so much, she was still not ready to live with him at this time, they still spent a lot of time with each other, staying at each other's places until Cassie got serious with her boyfriend then Anita moved back home with Mum and Dad.

Although Anita loved living at Cassie's, there was nothing like being back at home, back in her own cosy bedroom.

It was coming up to Anita and Mark's eighteenths and Mark proposed to Anita and they got engaged. One night Wayne asked

Mark to go to a club with him, he just wanted the lads without the girlfriends, as he didn't have anyone. This started happening more and more and Anita started to feel pushed out and upset with this. Someone else taking Mark's attention away from her, she didn't like one bit. Things started to change between them and they began to row over the slightest things. Anita thought she would be better off on her own and just longed for Mark's affection which seemed to change around his mates, whereas it never had before. In January 1985, Anita told Mark she didn't want to be with him any more she just couldn't cope with her feelings. Mark said, 'Well tell me you don't love me anymore first, then I'll walk away.'

Anita found it so hard, her heart wrenching inside and said 'I don't love you anymore.' Although she did so much. He was the most precious person in her life, but she thought it would be for the best. She waited for the front door to slam before bursting into tears and crying herself to sleep.

Chapter 5

The adrenalin drive

Anita began drinking heavily after work and weekends with her friends and didn't eat properly. She didn't know which day was what, and her heart felt excruciating pain for Mark, she just did not know what to do but drink it away. A lot of weekends, Anita spent with Cassie and the two of them would just get bladdered and go home to Cassie's and fall asleep. This went on for about three months and Anita seemed to find comfort in a bottle of scotch and her friends on a regular basis.

One day Anita's brother, Tom, was getting ready to go out with his friends, John and Barry. When they arrived to pick Tom up, John asked Anita what she was up to and did she want to come too. They all got in the car and John drove like a lunatic, and although she was frightened, it livened Anita up. This was like a big adrenalin rush, speeding through the lanes, not knowing if they were going to hit another car or vehicle head on or if they were going to come out the other end alive or not. At this point Anita really didn't care and started going out for more rides with John and they just eventually became an item. Anita's parents let her know that they did not approve of John and also told his parents in no uncertain terms, to which Anita rebelled.

Anita argued with her mum and dad so much over John and went to visit Aunt Rae with John. Aunt Rae asked Anita to move in with her and said that John could move in too, so they did. Aunt Rae told Anita that she wasn't keen on John but that she loved

Anita and wanted her to be happy. They lived at Aunt Rae's for a couple of months till they eventually got a flat of their own. Anita really appreciated Aunt Rae for helping her and loved spending time with her and the girls.

Moving in with John on her own, was a big step; she'd made her bed and now thought she had to lay in it, as the saying goes. Anita was so unhappy and tried so hard to be happy. Once moved into her own home with John, Anita got settled and decorated her home and was pleased with it. John spent a lot of time out with his friends, one night Anita was out in the car with them on the motorway, John started arguing with Anita in front of their friends and she had just had enough and thought, 'I can't take this anymore,' next thing Anita opened the car door to jump out, her friend screamed and grabbed her and John pulled over and put the child lock on and drove back home. Anita just cried and cried. John tried to comfort her but he didn't know why she was so unhappy. Anita just carried on and hoped for the best, she could not back down, however much it was hurting her.
John's family were lovely and Anita got on great with them, which made things worthwhile.

Anita and John had a very volatile relationship, arguing constantly most days, he was lazy and a womaniser. A few months passed to February 1986. Anita had been blacking out a lot and suffering from bad migraines. Anita went to the doctors for a check up. He sent her to the hospital, and Anita's mum went with her as Anita was very worried about what was wrong. She got the shock of her life when the consultant said 'Let me listen to your belly, I think you are pregnant.'

Anita was sixteen weeks pregnant, in shock and just cried inside her soul all the way home, thinking to herself 'This is so wrong, it should have been Mark's baby, I have fucked up my life having a baby with John.' She just desperately wanted Mark to come and find her and tell her everything would be alright. Instead, mum was with Anita telling her 'It will be ok, I'll help you,' and went home and had a good cry in the bath.

Although Anita was happy at being pregnant after the initial shock of it, there was no going back and she decided to make the best of it with John, even though people were telling her that he was seeing other women. Anita pushed this to the back of her mind, as now all that mattered now was her unborn child.

John was in disbelief at the news when Anita told him, saying that it wasn't his baby and that she must have been with someone else. Anita could not believe what she was hearing but just chose to ignore his remarks. That weekend it was John's friend Jay's twenty-first birthday. John and Anita arrived at the party. Anita told Jay the news, so Jay picked her up and spun her around congratulating them both. John was angry at this, then accused Anita of sleeping with Jay. Anita went home early on her own as she really did not want to be in John's company that evening.

A couple of days passed, Anita and John's friend, Biker Mark, had popped round for a chat. He was worried that his mum was having an affair and didn't know what to do or whether to tell his dad. He decided to wait until he knew for sure, then went home happier. The next day Anita received a phone call from Biker Mark, saying that he had just got home from work early and found his mum in bed with their friend, Gazza. He appeared to be in shock, Anita passed him to John, who told Biker Mark to come stay and with them for a while until he got his head together and decided what to do.

Biker Mark got on his motorbike and headed for their place. On the way, with his head all over the place and probably not concentrating properly, he pulled out of a turning and a bus went straight for him as he came off his motorbike, instantly fatally wounding Biker Mark.

Anita and John didn't find out for a couple of days as they thought he'd decided to stay at home when he didn't turn up. They were devastated when they heard the news. At the funeral, a week later, there were many of their friends and so many people crying. It was such a sad day.

Anita told John then that if the baby was a boy she wanted Mark in the name, John agreed, not realising Anita's reasoning although it was for both Marks.

John's dad rang John and asked if Anita and John would look after his fishing tackle shop while he went away with his girlfriend for two weeks on holiday. Next thing, Anita and John had packed up their belongings to move into the flat above the shop for the fortnight.

Anita had no experience of working in a tackle shop but quickly learned the ropes. She even got brave and put her hands in the maggot tub and did runs to the stinky maggot farm to stock up and deliver to other fishing tackle shops in the area.

Late one night, Anita received a phone call from Tom saying that their father was attacking their mother. Anita jumped up quickly and kept Tom on the phone whilst she got ready 'Dad's strangling Mum, and he hit me when I tried to get him off.' 'JOHN,' Anita screamed 'get the car keys; I need to get to my mum quick.' It was the quickest drive ever from the fishing tackle shop to where her mum lived. On arrival Anita banged on the door. Anita's dad answered the door. Without asking any questions Anita just hit out and punched her dad on the nose, telling him 'You leave my mum alone.' Anita called the police. Her mum wouldn't press charges so they left. Anita got John to go pick up Nan up and stop with her mum and called dad's brothers who came round and told him whatever, while calming him down and took him home with them for the night.

Anita stayed with her mum and nan for a while to make sure her mum was ok before heading back to the shop.

The next morning Anita rang her mum to make sure she was ok. Nan had decided to stop for a few days with her mum, so that put Anita at ease.

The shop was busy that day and time seemed to go quickly. John left Anita in the shop on her own for a lot of the time and just made sure he was back in time for banking the money. The two weeks soon passed and the time came to go back home with John. Anita was not really looking forward to this, although she carried on regardless.

Back home in the flat, Anita decided she should be getting the flat decorated and ready for her baby which was due in the summer. Anita really enjoyed getting things ready for the baby coming and painted her bedroom and put a cot in next to the patio doors that led out to the garden. Anita decided to paint the bathroom next and Sarah, John's sister, came to help. Whilst they were busy painting away, John arrived home with a duckling and said he just bought it. He hadn't even thought about a run or anything for it.

Anita named the duckling Snowy. Soon it was following Anita around everywhere in the flat. One day it wouldn't come in from the garden so Anita couldn't lock it up and John just left it outside. Next thing a fox got it. Anita was very upset at this and blamed John for being too lazy to get it in.

Anita and John's flat soon became a drop-in centre for John's scooter friends. It seemed to Anita that she hardly had five minutes to herself.

John came home with his friends, Harry and Max, one day, thinking that they were all gangster-like bragging about safe cracking. Anita just giggled to herself and thought what idiots at the time. Paul, another of John's friends, used to pop in a lot. You could hear his scooter as it seemed to make a weird sound compared to the rest. He used to act so stupid and sing 'Eric the half a bee, dum dum dum dee dee dee,' which made Anita laugh so much because it was so stupid.

One night a few friends came round for a drink, Anita didn't know some of them, Anita's friend, Shell, ended up having sex with Harry on the sofa, with a couple of other friends in the room watching, whilst pretending to be asleep. Meanwhile, John had gone to take home a couple of girls that Anita didn't know. He was gone a while.

Anita just focused on becoming a mum and hoped things would get better, and although John was a loser, Anita had begun to love his family very much, especially Sarah. She helped Anita a lot and they spent a lot of time together. Anita's daughter, Christina, was born in the summer. Anita couldn't believe she was actually a mum, how was she going to cope? She didn't know anything about being a mum and thought she wouldn't be able to manage. The first week Anita just kept looking at this little persona and felt so much love for her and now Christina was the most precious thing in her life, although not forgetting Mark, it was a different kind of love. Sarah was a great help; she stayed with Anita to help her settle in with the baby, after all, this little person was her niece and a strong bond soon developed between Sarah and Christina. John actually surprised everyone and was a good dad in the beginning, eventually his disappearance for hours on end became too much.

Anita began to confide in her friend Jamie, whom she'd known since childhood. Jamie sympathised with Anita and began to stay a lot. One day John came in and said he had been to his dad's and that his dad had suggested that they exchange their flats, as Anita and John lived in a one bedroom flat and his dad lived in a two bedroom flat just off the Old Kent Road. Anita wasn't too keen on this, as she didn't want to be away from her friends and knew she would be on her own when John did his disappearing acts. Eventually John and his dad talked her round reluctantly and they swapped with his dad, with John and his dad saying they would sort out the paperwork later. Anita naively agreed. When they swapped, John's sister, Sonya, was staying with her dad, so this still left them without an extra bedroom for the baby. Anita hated living away from her friends and on her own a lot with a young baby. She then found out that the flat wasn't even John's dad's to swap with in the first place, and so had to try to find a way to sort it out to stay there. This left Anita so confused and not knowing which way to turn, but Jamie kept telling her things would be alright.

They spent that Christmas at John's mum's and had a lovely day. Early next morning, there was a big bang at the front door. It had been kicked in by the police who had a warrant for John for non payment of fines and motoring offences. They arrested him and sent him straight to court, giving him four months in Pentonville prison. 'Oh my God,' Anita thought, 'what am I going to do now.' She rang her mum and told her what had happened. Her mum told her to go back home with Christina. So Anita went back, not knowing what to do. It was so nice being back home with mum and Tom and Christina. John sent Anita visiting orders to go with his mum. Anita wore leggings and a blue top, trying to look nice. She was scared at the thought of going to a prison let alone visiting someone there.

John's mum, Val, arrived to pick Anita up; they set off taking Christina with them. Anita and Val chatted all the way, both very anxious at the thought of going to a prison. When they finally arrived on Pentonville Road, Anita wasn't sure whether to go in or not, then Val reassured her that it would be ok once they got inside.

When they arrived they showed the visiting order, then they went through some gates with the guard who showed them where to wait whilst the prisoners were all shown to their tables, also to wait.

John came in the room and sat at the table unshaven, and his uncut hair looking rough. Val and Anita took Christina over to the table and started making small talk as they didn't really know what to say with everyone around and the guards watching, even though they were not doing anything wrong. It was just the atmosphere of the place. Some prisoners were arguing with their visitors and got sent back to their cells. Val asked John how they were treating him in there, he replied 'Good, and I've made a few friends,' which didn't surprise Anita at all. Anita told him that Christina had started saying dada and had wanted her to say mum first instead, which broke the ice between them and they started talking about the family.

John told Anita that she looked like a hooker, which upset Anita terribly. How could the father of her child say that to her she thought, but carried on and hoped for the best for Christina's sake.

Time soon passed and it was time for John to come out. Mum didn't want him living there with them so they moved in with her sister Diane for a while. Whilst John had been inside, Anita put her name down on a council housing list. After a couple of months staying at Diane's, Christina had a cold and Anita, checking on her throughout, found her not breathing and blue around her mouth. Anita panicked and screamed for John. John immediately came, turned Christina upside down and patted her back whilst Diane was on the phone to the ambulance. Christina started breathing again and went into hospital staying in for the night. It was because of a high temperature. Christina had appeared to have had a fit and stopped breathing. John just did the right thing and was lucky he saved Christina that day. Anita and John appeared to be getting closer together, or so Anita thought, and it was a kind of loving between them, but the rows soon started again. Then one day Anita got a letter from the housing to view a flat. It was a two bedroom, on the tenth floor of a tower block in Bromley. Anita went to view it and took the flat as it was near her friends and family and easy for her to get into town. Although it was in a tower block, Anita loved this flat even if she was home alone with Christina, as she thought she could get out and about and Jamie visited a lot more often. Soon, Anita decided to take driving lessons, and Jamie came to look after Christina while she was having lessons. One day Christina told Anita daddy kissed Auntie Jamie at the park. Anita could not believe what she was hearing. No not Jamie and John, but it must be, a two year old wouldn't lie about this, she wouldn't know to do that.

Anita confronted them both, but they both denied it. Anita had just about had enough and threw him out and told him to take all his things or she would throw them off the balcony of the tenth floor. Anita was more hurt losing her friendship with Jamie as they had been such good friends and confided in each other.

Mum was there yet again for Anita, picking up the pieces, stepping in and babysitting whenever and just generally spending time with Anita and Christina.

Anita soon pulled herself together and Sarah spent more time with them, taking Christina out and about with her. Anita was so glad of Sarah's friendship, she didn't know what she would have done without her, also her mum, pulling together and helping her. She felt so much love for them both. Anita tried to sort out visits for Christina, even with Jamie there along with John, for Christina's sake. John was not turning up for his visits which upset Christina and then he turned up sometimes when she was in bed asleep. Anita went to a solicitor to arrange proper access times for John because of this, and John sent the letters back, not known at this address. 'The contact with John's family continued as they loved the little girl so much and it was a strong bond even with Sonya who didn't seem the least bit maternal.

In the meantime, unbeknown to Anita, Mark was having a tough time.

Anita decided to stay on her own for a couple of years and concentrate on her daughter.

I need a night out thought Anita, and rang her friends, Lily and Ellie. They suggested going to The Swan and Sugarloaf, in

Croydon as it was a Rockers night and should be a laugh. So all 3 got ready and got a taxi there. Anita got chatting to a guy who did a bit of DJ work. He was also a member of the Lib Dems. Nev, asked Anita on a date, with Lily and Ellie egging her on. She said ok and went for a drink with him the next day at the local pub. Nev lived near Margate so wouldn't get to see much of her at all, Anita thought, which suited her fine.

A romance really was not on the agenda, just having a laugh and making sure Christina was looked after well were Anita's main concerns. Anita took Sarah with her when visiting Nev, as Anita didn't want to be on her own. Nev's outlook on life was to work for 6 months and have 6 months off and live life. It soon fizzled out as Nev wanted romance and marriage, Anita only wanted to see Nev on her own terms as she had Christina to think about, and knew there would never be any love on her part, so finished it after a short while. Nev told Anita that she was lucky to have him, as no one else would want her with a child already. Anita liked being independent and not having anyone to answer to, especially not a jerk like Nev.

Anita carried on with life and got a part time job, working with her friend Sabrina in a nursing home. Whilst Anita was at work, Diane looked after Christina. Anita loved being back at work, although she loved Christina deeply, it was the adult conversation away from the flat that Anita needed.

Anita and Diane were getting on very well and took the children to the park regularly and Anita liked this very much. Things were looking up, Anita still missed Mark in her life but thought there was no going back or Mark would have come looking for her. She felt sad at this, and smiled, remembering times together with Mark.

Chapter 6

The wedding

Somewhere around 1990, Anita kept bumping into her friend Harry a lot. He made her laugh and offered to babysit if Anita wanted to go out. Harry began to pop around to Anita's often. Anita found herself telling Harry about her feelings for Mark and that she knew she had made a big mistake leaving Mark and it felt like she had an empty space in her life she couldn't fill.

Harry asked Anita out for dinner one day, with Christina as well. Anita thought 'Why not, he gets on well with Christina and makes me laugh.' Harry spent so much time at Anita's his mother took offence and kicked Harry out, so Anita let him move in as he didn't have anywhere else to go, and they did get on well. Harry wined and dined Anita taking her to restaurants, often taking Christina as well, and the staff commented on what a well behaved child Christina was. In the summer, Anita had Christina christened. Harry's sister, Patsy, helped Anita prepare all the food for the christening. Anita and Patsy had become good friends, even before Anita was with Harry.

Harry made Anita laugh a lot and they got on really well. Soon Anita found herself falling for Harry and looked forward to him coming in from work. She thought to herself 'Is this love?' It's so different from Mark whom she had never stopped loving.

Anita went to the shops one day with Christina, then into town. Whilst out, she kept bumping into the same person and on her way home they both went into the same tower block. Anita laughed and said to the woman jokingly 'Are you following me?' Immediately they struck up a friendship.

'I'm Fiona, I take it you live here too.'

'Yes,' replied Anita.

Soon they started taking their children out together and to nursery. Their children got on well. Anita found it hard to confide in another woman after her friend Jamie, but found Fiona so easy to get on with they both began telling each other all about their lives and problems, and generally having a good laugh about things.

One day, out of the blue, Christina started calling Harry 'daddy.' Anita was overwhelmed at her little girl calling someone else daddy. Harry thought this was great and quite liked it.

A few weeks later, whilst Christina was asleep in bed, Anita was relaxing in a bubble bath; Harry came in and proposed to Anita. Anita couldn't believe what she was hearing as she really never expected to even think about getting married at this stage in her life. However she found herself saying yes.

Harry wanted to get married in the church just along the road, so they went to see the vicar, who they already knew from the christening and nursery school, and booked the wedding for February 1992. In May of 1991, Anita felt unwell and found out that she was pregnant, and due two weeks before the wedding. She started to panic in case she was overdue, so cancelled the church and rebooked at the Registry Office. In the summer Anita miscarried the baby, which left her distraught and she wouldn't go out not even to take Christina to school. Harry took over, and

Sarah helped out until Anita was back on track. Patsy was great and comforted Anita over the miscarriage. Although Anita really didn't want any more children, the fact of falling pregnant and then losing the baby started her maternal clock ticking, she decided she would like to have another child after all, at some time.

Although Anita got on really well with Patsy, the rest of Harry's family were not all so warm towards her and were very clichy and bitchy. Why they were like that Anita had no idea as she had always been friendly towards them, and never bitched to any of them about each other, although they all talked about each other to Anita.

Anita sometimes thought 'Are some of these people for real.' The women were the worst in the family for bitching between each other, and Anita never felt comfortable around some of them. What made it worse was Harry never showed Anita any affection around them, never kissed or cuddled her in front of them and she could not understand why. Mark would never have done this and to this day Anita stilled missed Mark.

Christina was getting ill a lot with chest infections, and then was diagnosed asthmatic. As there was a lot of damp in the flat after the council re-roofed the tower block because of a leak, and also being on the top floor, the council offered Anita a house. Anita could not wait to get the keys and moved in as soon as possible. It was great having a garden and a driveway, and in a quiet street and still in easy reach of town. Christina started a new school which she loved and she made lots of friends and became very popular, going to friends for tea after school and having them come home with her for tea. It was a lovely time. Anita was really happy.

It was New Year's Eve, and Harry's sister, Jade, was having a party. Anita was not keen on going until Harry said that Sarah was invited too. This made Anita happier about going to the party as she wasn't keen on some of Jade's friends who would be there. Once at the party, Anita and Sarah stayed together all evening and there were a lot of Welsh people there who Anita and Sarah found very amusing. As the clock struck midnight, they both went round saying 'Happy New year, have a leek,' to them all. The leek being the Welsh emblem along with the dragon. The humour stayed with them as they walked home, and they continued saying it to everyone they passed in the street, thinking that they also found it amusing.

Harry did not find it very funny and shouted at Anita the next morning. Anita didn't care as she was just very hung over and didn't get up until Christina came and jumped into bed with her.

Things were moving along and it wasn't long before Harry and Anita's wedding. Mum helped out a lot. Harry's mother had picked a wedding dress for Anita. Anita felt that the wedding was just being taken over, all she wanted was to go away and get married with no fuss and just have a holiday, then a party to come home to, but it wasn't to be. The night before the wedding, Fiona stayed with Anita and helped her get everything ready and sort out her dress and Christina's dress.

The morning of the wedding, Anita was so nervous and said to Fiona 'I'm not sure I'm doing the right thing, I don't know if I can do it.' Fiona told her that everything would be ok and put Anita at ease and gave her a large glass of brandy. At the Registry Office Anita told Fiona that she felt like a big blancmange. Fiona laughed and said she looked beautiful. Cousin Frankie was standing with them with his wife, Toni, Auntie Floss and cousin Katy; they had all come over from Canada.

Christina made everyone laugh by telling them she was marrying daddy. Christina was the only bridesmaid, so Anita didn't have to choose between nephews and nieces or friends' children, it just made it easier.

The day went well, although Anita didn't remember half of it as she got so drunk. Her mum took Christina home for the night. When Anita and Harry arrived home, they forgot to get their door keys from Frankie as he had locked up for Anita. Unfortunately he had driven home up north with them. Harry found a window open, so Anita had to climb in the window in her wedding dress but couldn't open the front door till Diane came around the next morning with the spare set of keys, which amused the neighbours.

A couple of weeks after the wedding, Harry kept on popping out to the shops and coming back late, when Anita asked him where he had been, he said he been he said he had popped into his friend Trisha's for a cuppa. Anita had never heard of her until now. When at the shop with Harry a couple of days later, they bumped into Trisha, Harry introduced her to Anita and took Trisha's phone number.

Harry started popping to Trisha's more and more, when questioned, he said he felt sorry for her being a single parent and he smoked joints with her. Never mind that Anita was alone with Christina. Next time Harry went to Trisha's, Anita found the phone number and rang asking if Harry was there. Trisha replied 'I don't know, are you here Harry? I think it's your wife.' Then he went home to a massive argument. Anita thinking 'What have I done marrying him.' She wanted to make it work as she really didn't want to be another divorce statistic. She tried so hard, despite many rows and screaming and shouting at each other.

A year later they moved house to get Harry away from popping into Trisha's. He would have to get a bus now, so probably wouldn't go so often. Things seemed to calm down. Anita got a job around Harry's, so they didn't need childcare and still kept things going in the house. Anita's life felt very empty as there was still something missing and she thought maybe going to church and being nearer God may help. Anita tried and tried to no avail to fill the empty space that she felt. She made lots of friends at the church and the pastor pulled her to one side one day and told her that he could see that he could see that there were problems in her marriage and would she like to go to marriage counselling with Harry. Anita gave it a go but it didn't last as Harry just blamed Anita for everything which explained his attitude towards her.

One Sunday dinner time, whilst Anita, Harry and Christina were just about to eat dinner, Harry decided to say Grace and insisted if Christina wishes to she can,' But don't force it on her. 'I don't want to' Christina said that she didn't want to either.

At this, Harry just tipped the table up so the dinners were smashed on the floor and then started screaming abuse at Anita. He told Anita he did not like her working and not being at home. Anita looked into doing child minding at home and registered herself. Then Harry wanted Anita to have a baby.

After a year of trying, Anita did not fall pregnant again and got checked. They found that her fallopian tubes were blocked, which could have happened from her miscarrying before her marriage. Anita was told the only way that she would be able to have another child would be to have IVF treatment.

The IVF treatment was very difficult, having to inject hormones into herself at certain times and going to the hospital to be checked, with her legs in stirrups, whilst the doctor put an internal probe inside Anita, for all and sundry who walked in the room to see. The fact that it was only nursing staff didn't make it any more dignified, but just added to the embarrassment that Anita felt. The IVF did not work the first time.

Anita went for a second attempt at IVF. One of Harry's brother's girlfriend's, accused Anita and Harry's brother of having an affair, which was absolutely absurd. Anita did not treat Harry's brothers any differently to her own brother and for God's sake, was going through IVF with Harry. This time did not work either. Harry wanted Anita to go for a third attempt but Anita refused.

After having a good think to herself, about Harry actually thinking that she may have been having an affair with his brother, and doubting Anita. No way was she going to bring another child into this relationship, and would only do a third attempt if and when completely happy within herself.

Anita popped round to Diane's for lunch one afternoon. Diane was very upset as she found out that the bowel cancer, that her husband had been in remission from, had progressed and the condition was now terminal. Anita did not know what to do or say to comfort her sister as there was nothing anyone could do, except just be there for her. Diane needed a couple of days out to get herself together, so Anita and Diane took the children to Pontin's Holiday Camp for a weekend. The children had a great time. Diane appeared more relaxed, although very worried about leaving her husband, Callum, for a couple of days, although he was in capable hands with his sister. On return, things carried on as usual and

Callum went into hospital for treatment. One morning, whilst getting ready to go to the hospital, a news flash came up, Diana, The Princess of Wales, died in a car crash. Across the country people mourned everywhere, it was a sad time. When Anita and Diane arrived to visit Callum, he said that he had been to put flowers at the memorial place for the Princess and really believed he had. Anita thought maybe he had had an out of body experience and really did that; it was so real to him.

Callum insisted on coming home after this. So Diane had him brought home. He was in so much pain and so weak. Anita could see the hurt in her sister's eyes just watching as her husband was slowly dying in front of her. The week after the Princess's death, late one evening, Callum passed away, holding Diane's hand. It was such a heartbreaking time for Diane and the children.

At the funeral Diane held her head high as she loved her husband so much and was very proud of him. Many people came to pay their respects.

Life carried on. Diane mourned her husband but had to carry on as normal for the children. Anita admired Diane's strength at this time in her life and tried to help where she could, even if it just meant looking after the children.

A couple of years after this, Anita's great grandmother died. Anita was devastated as she really loved her and started to question her own life, thinking things needed to change. The first thing that changed was Anita looked for a new job as she wanted back her independence. Harry would have to like it or lump it. 'I'm not having him telling me to stay at home,' she thought to herself.

Anita found a new job almost immediately. It was as if the job was waiting for her to come along and start, it was just perfect. So Anita gave up child minding.

There was a knock at the door, Anita answered. It was Fiona popping round for a cup of tea and a chat. Fiona told Anita that she was planning to go to Spain for a week and that her partner did not want to go and would Anita, Harry and Christina like to go with her? Harry refused point blank. Anita said she would like to go. 'Great,' said Fiona 'It's just me, you and the children then Anita.' Wow, thought Anita how good was this going to be. Fiona looked into the booking of it and they decided to go by coach as it was a lot cheaper. Anita had a couple of weeks before she started her new job. so they decided to go before then. Anita was looking forward to it so much and went shopping in town and bought herself and Christina some holiday clothes. Fiona had arranged for her father to drop them off to Victoria Coach Station. The night before, Anita and Christina went to bed early as they had an early start. Fiona knocked early the next morning for them with her father, so off to Victoria Coach Station they went.

They arrived they were very early and had an hour to wait, so went for a coffee. Soon it was time for them all to board the coach, as they were the first one's on, they all sat along the back seat. Spirits were high among all the passengers and the tour guide was bringing soup and hot drinks around to the passengers.

They soon arrived in Dover and had to stay on the coach whilst it boarded the ferry. Once on, they all got off and went around and sat in the lounge with snacks for the children.

Time soon passed and they arrived in France and all boarded the coach again.

Driving through France was an experience and tiresome, so they decide to have a nap.

After a few hours they arrived in Spain and were dropped off at their hotel in Pineda. They checked in and took all their things to their rooms and before going, down for their dinners. The dinner was buffet style so they all had whatever they wanted. That evening, the hotel had laid on a Spanish dance which they all watched, after that it was a children's disco, soon they went to bed exhausted with all the travelling.

The next morning Anita and Christina got up, showered, got ready and went and knocked for Fiona, Louly and Sharn (Fiona's children). They all went down to breakfast together. After breakfast, they all had a good look around the hotel, there was an outdoor pool on the roof. 'Brill,' said Fiona 'we shall be up here later with our books.' Then they all went out of the hotel to find the beach. Fiona brought her rubber ring with her for paddling. When they got to the beach they all applied suntan cream and lay down to sunbathe. Anita grabbed Fiona's rubber ring and went and floated in the sea. Whilst coming back out of the sea Anita left the rubber ring around her waist. Fiona saw this and started laughing and asked her why she was doing this. Anita said to hide her flabby bits. Fiona found this hilarious and was laughing for ages; it even made the girls all laugh. They stayed at the beach until tea time then set off back to the hotel. Louly and Christina were chatting away to some local boys and got chatting to the waiters. Sharn read her books. Fiona and Anita got a bit tiddly and giggly.

The next day they decided to check out the town and, looking around the shops, spent ages. Then they found a MacDonald's restaurant so just had to go in with the girls, then back to the shops. Christina saw a bb gun which she wanted. Anita told her she didn't know if she would get through customs with it, but Christina bought it anyway. The week had soon passed and it was time to go home. Returning home they got through customs ok on the coach, so Christina kept her bb gun which she was pleased with.

Chapter 7

New friends

Anita's new job was working at a special needs school for children with cerebral palsy. Anita absolutely loved this job and made some really good friends, two in particular were Lea and Tracey. The friends would just pop round to each other's for a cup of tea or pop into town for lunch and have barbecues in the summer. Anita felt like she had her life back again and she loved it.

Christina by now was a teenager. Harry and Anita argued over his methods of raising her, Anita could see no wrong in how Christina was and Harry argued with Anita for not backing him up, but Anita couldn't when she could see he was totally wrong.

One day Anita's mum popped round. Anita got on great with her mum as she was always there for her. Mum told Anita that Nan wanted to go to Australia to see Uncle Rick and Nan thought it would be the last time she would make the journey because of her age. She asked if Anita and Christina would like to go. Anita jumped at the chance and started saving to go to Australia. In February 2000 they flew out to Australia, stopping in Bangkok on the way. Anita, Mum and Christina all went to the toilet when the plane landed but as Nan didn't want to go to the toilet; she sat and waited until they got back. When they got back to get Nan she wasn't there, how could she disappear in a wheelchair? They searched everywhere in the airport finally finding Nan with a steward in the airport lounge. By this time they were soon to board the plane again.

The plane finally landed in Australia and all the family were at the airport to meet them. Jetlag set in so they all went to bed early. The next morning Anita felt relaxed, not having a care in the world and was in holiday mode. She thought to herself 'So many unexplored shops,' and shared her thought with Christina who agreed with her, so they went to the shopping mall with her cousins and had all the time in the world to explore. Christina was in her element with mum buying her lots of clothes they don't have back home.

The next day they went to the beach and, through their sunglasses, secretly checked out the fit bodies on the beach, it was only fun and just having a laugh. In the sea, having to avoid the jelly fish was a chore, but nevertheless it was fun, just what they needed. Anita wished she could stay here forever, in the sun away from reality.

Up early the next morning, with the sun shining. Uncle Rick decided everyone was going to the wildlife park for the day. Nan wanted to go too. So after breakfast everyone set off to the park. Anita and Christina were in their element, seeing the Koalas and Kangaroos up close and stroking them, and thoroughly enjoyed their day out. On return, Uncle Rick and Aunt Lin got the barbecue ready. Cousins Das and Richie came round for tea with their wives Paula and Dani. Paula was a beautiful Portuguese girl and Dani was Australian and very funny and beautiful. Anita got on well with both of them. Christina thought a lot of Paula, Paula made a fuss of Christina as she did not have a daughter of her own, only a son Jack. Paula and Christina spent time chatting for hours and doing make up and clothes shopping together. One day whilst in the mall, some teenage lads were all looking at Christina. Das told them to go away and leave his little cousin alone. Anita thought it was funny that Das was being protective of her daughter. That evening everyone made a fuss of Nan, moisturising her feet and legs, just generally pampering Nan, as Nan just seemed so tired out and breathless all the time.

Anita told Das and Paula that she would like to do a bungee jump. Das said that he would take her into Perth where he knew of a place where they did bungee jumps and he would take her tomorrow if she wanted. At the bungee park, all the family came to watch Anita. Anita was weighed and then had to sign a consent form, so then off she went, climbing the steps up the tower with two other people doing a jump. Finally, up the top of the tower. Anita was knackered. Another woman was supposed to go before Anita but refused to go as she bottled out. So it was Anita's turn. All strapped up to the bungee rope Anita went to the edge of the tower, looking down you could see for miles and such a big drop. 'When you're ready,' shouted the bungee master and Anita just jumped, free falling, it was like nothing she had ever experienced before just falling and nothing she could do about it now. 'Wow it's wicked' shouted out Anita.

'You're crazy,' Das shouted up to her with everyone clapping.

Anita was swinging upside down till someone came and lowered her down and put her into a boat to take her back, still rushing with adrenalin, Anita thought 'Wow I did it.' That evening Anita had few drinks with the family.

The holiday soon came to an end and when saying their goodbyes to the family, Christina was nowhere to be found. Eventually she came out from under the bed where she had hiding not wanting to go back either.

Arriving back home, they settled back into normal routine. Anita saw more of her friends and spent lots more time with them, in and out of work. Harry didn't like this new independent Anita, as she was doing things without him, shopping and lunching with the girls.

A year passed and it was summer. Harry was exceptionally weird, wanting to go to lunch with Anita and the girls, like he was trying to catch her out at something. He would embarrass Anita in front of her friends by being really crude, thinking he was funny. Christina started going to her friends a lot more and staying over, then she met a guy and started dating him. She didn't take him home and Harry did not like this, or the fact that his little girl was all grown up, so he took an instant dislike to Christina's boyfriend and told Christina that she wasn't allowed to see him anymore, which of course caused an argument between them. Harry was getting exceptionally controlling. Christina decided to go across to her nan's as she would understand and listen. Harry was not having any of this and started to restrain Christina on the stairs. Anita told him to leave her alone and let her go across to her nan but there was no reasoning with Harry and he shoved Christina on the stairs. Anita tried pulling him away, he told Anita to 'Fuck off you cunt.' That was it; Anita lashed out and hit him. He immediately let go of Christina and started punching Anita in the head, blow after blow, with such force, Anita fell to the ground and managed to get herself in the corner and cover her head. Christina ran out of the door and across to her nan's. Anita just sat still for a short while, in shock, before managing to get up slowly and walk down to her mum's, which seemed like forever although only a two minute walk. She had tears streaming down her face and her head felt numb, she was shaking all over with shock. When she arrived at her mum's, Christina was already there, crying. Anita just broke down and cried relentlessly and mum just cuddled her and begged

Anita to leave Harry and be happy. Anita now had her mind set on leaving him but needed to do it properly and sort things out. Harry didn't speak to Anita for a couple of days, so Anita just carried on going to work as usual. Harry slept on the sofa. Anita was on a late back to back with an early shift and when she got home from the late Harry was asleep on the sofa as usual, so Anita went up to bed. Christina was asleep in her room. Anita got her clothes ready for early shift next morning and went to sleep.

At 3am, Anita was woken by a scream, it was strange it was getting quieter. Anita checked Christina who was asleep. Maybe Christina had been dreaming and screamed in her sleep. Anita called out to Harry but got no answer, so went downstairs to check, he was laying strangely on the sofa with an arm underneath his stomach and suddenly a moment of fear came over Anita, wondering what he had done. Anita tried to wake Harry but he was foaming from his mouth. Anita rang 999 straight away and the operator told her to put Harry in the recovery position. Then Anita noticed two tablets on the floor and an empty box which was full the day before. The paramedics arrived in no time and took Harry straight to ICU and told Anita that it appeared he had swallowed all the tablets and if he was lucky he would live another forty-eight hours at the most. They decided to put him on a drip and try to flush him through ,although they didn't hold out much hope. Anita rang Fiona and Patsy; they were soon at the hospital by her side and rang round family and friends for Anita, who all visited in stages to say their goodbyes to Harry. Miraculously Harry pulled through and survived. According to the psychiatrists there would be no long term effects.

The psychiatrist recommended to Anita, that she sent Christina to stay with a family member whilst Harry was on the mend, and that he thought Anita should put Harry's needs first. 'No way,' said Anita, 'I'm not putting anyone before my child and certainly not making her leave home.'

The psychiatrist asked Anita to stay at the hospital for a night as Harry was so anxious when Anita was not around for even 2 minutes. Anita agreed to stay for one night. She didn't tell Harry's family or friends that he had overdosed out of guilt for beating her up. She felt too ashamed to tell the truth and kept quiet saying she didn't know why he did it. Obviously Anita's mother knew and her sister and Fiona, who she confined in.

Harry just blatantly lied and put the blame on Christina telling the psychiatrist that she was out of control, and he could not cope any more. Harry then emotionally blackmailed Anita in staying. She would not be able to forgive herself if he killed himself because of her, so she thought she should try and give her marriage another go and put on a front. Months passed by and Anita and Harry celebrated their tenth wedding anniversary. They took trips away up north with Christina and Anita decided she wanted to move up north and began looking for a job online.

Chapter 8

The move

As luck would have it, Anita got 3 interviews the same day and got the jobs, so now moving north was becoming a reality. Harry's mother at this time, was not too well, so Anita suggested that she and Christina move up north and Harry move in with his mother for a while, to look after her before he moved with them. Harry, worried about his mother, went for the idea.

What great news that was for Anita, living apart from Harry, having time to herself. The move went great. That summer Fiona visited a lot and so did Tracey and Lucy. Anita just threw herself into work the rest of the time and spent time with Christina who settled into college and made friends easily. Anita soon made some good friends at work called Maggie and Annabelle after working with them only a short time. They just seemed to click; it was like a different life. Anita didn't tell them her reasons for wanting to be away from Harry, how could she, it was embarrassing that she stayed with a man who hit her, let alone give in to his emotional blackmail. One day at work, the boss was asking for volunteers to take the children on holiday. Anita put her name forward straight away and so did Maggie and Annabelle. They all had such fun taking the children away for the week. Maggie and Annabelle noticed cracks in Anita's marriage although Anita still did not tell them. Time had passed and Anita loved being able to do her own thing when she wanted and not having to answer to anyone and only sort herself and Christina. One day Christina asked if she could have a dog, so they went and picked a puppy and named him Charlie. He was so good for Anita and went everywhere with her and was a great companion. Anita spent a lot of time on the beach with him. A few months passed and Harry rang and said instead of just coming for a weekend visit like usual, he was moving up for good. Anita was apprehensive about this but thought to herself that she was married after all and if she tried to make the best of it, maybe things might get better.

Harry moved up. Things were great for a few weeks and Harry settled into work and wined and dined Anita, which went well. After a few months, the cracks started to resurface. Harry accused Anita of having an affair with someone at work. Anita could not believe what she was hearing. This pushed Anita into doing more hours at work and filling her days off with lunches with the girls. Christina and her friends went too. One night Maggie and Annabelle were going into town and asked Anita to go with them, so they picked Anita up on the way. A couple of hours passed and Harry rang Anita, screaming and shouting on the phone, accusing Anita of being with another man, then said he was coming to get her. Next thing he's in the club, nearly dragging Anita out by her arm in front of Maggie and Annabelle. Walking home he called Anita a whore. He pulled Anita along the street by her hair threatening to punch her, 'Go on then,' said Anita. 'If you are going to beat me up, just do it, you are already on camera pulling my hair.' With tears running down her face she was terrified at the thought of being home alone with Harry, knowing that Christina was staying at her friends. When back in the house Harry demanded sex, Anita just thought it was easier to give in as she was afraid of what he might do to her. By this time she felt sick at the thought of him putting his hands on her body and tried to just blank herself into no emotion.

The next morning Anita got up early when Harry went to work, she took Charlie for a walk on the beach and started praying 'Please God, please help me, please let Mark come and find me and take me away. I know I fucked up my life when I walked out on Mark, please let him still love me,' and then she cried hysterically along the beach.

Life continued as it had to, being married. Although there were very difficult times, as Anita did not want to be there and just tried to blank things out to stay happy. Harry started to go out a lot; he was with friends from work. He went out most nights and came in late and then accused Anita of having affairs. When Anita asked who specifically he was out with, he just kept saying work friends, partners are not invited. This started Anita thinking, as he was constantly accusing her of having affairs, was he having an affair himself, or was he just ashamed of her. Also his aggression verbally was getting worse. Anita didn't say anything to this and just walked on eggshells for what seemed like a lifetime, never knowing what mood he would be in when he got home. Anita started dreading the door going when she knew it was Harry.

Sometimes Anita pretended to be asleep when Harry got home, just so as not to have sex with him, then he just started to force himself upon her when he wanted, even when Anita said 'No let me sleep,' even using the excuse of having to be up early in the morning. This continued for months.

Anita just so much looked forward to going to work and volunteered to do the sleepovers no one wanted to do, just to be away from home. One early morning of the sleepovers, the phone rang at 5am. Annabelle answered the phone and went and woke Anita up as it was Harry. He told Anita to get home right away he had fallen down the stairs and hurt himself. Anita asked if he could walk ok and as he could, she told him to get an ambulance as she couldn't just walk out of work. He said it would be too late, he would be dead by the time she finished her shift. Anita had to then tell Annabelle what had happened and Annabelle sent Anita home and covered for her. Harry was taken into hospital and kept in for the week. Anita spoke to the psychiatrist about Harry, telling him she thought he threw himself down the stairs and the psychiatrist said 'Unless he admits he has a problem, there is nothing I can do.' That was not good enough for Anita but at least she had a week's peace whilst he was in the hospital.

Time passed and Diane met someone new and was getting married again. Anita was very happy for them both as they seemed to be very happy and so much in love. Diane asked Anita to be a bridesmaid. Anita accepted. The wedding was lovely, family and friends from across the world came, Anita was having a good time until Harry started harassing her and being nasty, even shouting at her in front of the guests, just humiliating her. Anita was so ashamed and just didn't know what to do. That evening when she got home, she just cried and let the dog sleep in the bed with her so she felt safe.

The next morning Harry did not show any remorse for his actions and told Anita she just deserved what she got after the way she treated him. 'What planet was he on,' Anita thought, 'Where on Earth does he get these crazy ideas? May be he is schizophrenic. All these things just went round in her head.

There was a knock on the door, Anita answered, it was Louise; she popped round to see if Anita wanted to go for lunch while she was in town. Anita had too much to do today and didn't have time to go out as she needed to catch up with the washing and cleaning, so asked Louise to stay for lunch with her there. Louise was meeting some friends so declined at this point and went after a brew. Ten minutes later there was another knock at the door, Anita answered. Another friend from work, Layla, was at the door shaking and crying and appeared to be in shock. Anita brought Layla into the house. Harry came in at the moment Anita was asking Layla what was wrong. Layla said that she had been having an affair with another woman at work and that someone else had found out and that the woman she was having the affair with was denying everything as she was a married woman. Layla was absolutely distraught at this and told Anita who it was and swore her to secrecy that she wouldn't tell the woman that she knew about it. Layla stopped and had tea with Anita and Harry, who thought, this was very amusing. When Layla seemed to calm down, she drove home and rang Anita and thanked her for her support. Harry started laughing and said he could not believe what he had heard. Anita asked him not to mention it to anyone but was not sure whether he would or not.

Chapter 9

Please leave him

A few months later Dad passed and Anita's mum had to go into hospital for an operation, which would mean she needed looking after to help her recovery. After her mum's operation, Anita drove down and picked her up from the hospital and brought her home to look after her. Anita's mum needed help getting showered and dressed. Whilst Anita was doing this, and working full time as well, one of Anita's friends, Louise, rang, and asked if she would like to go to a wedding with her as she was allowed to take a friend and didn't have anyone to go with, being single. Anita said 'Ok that would be great but I cannot stay late, as I have to look after my mum.' Harry did not like this as he said Anita was using this as an excuse to go and see whoever she was having an affair with. Anita just thought to herself, it was not worth the hassle going and rang Louise back and said 'Thinking about it, I cannot go, I've got too much to do with Mum,' as an excuse. That night Harry started an argument, not caring that Anita's mum was in the house and could hear everything. He punched Anita whilst she was sitting in bed, of course hearing all this made her mum cry. The next morning when Harry was at work, Mum begged Anita once again to leave Harry and that it would make Anita ill in the end. Anita told her mum she would have to do it in her own time and when he could no longer emotionally blackmail her. Anita had to be in the right frame of mind.

A couple of weeks later Anita took her mum home and stayed with her for the weekend. Anita, dreading the thought of going back home. Harry then accused Anita of having an affair with someone near her mum. This was ludicrous to Anita who was looking after her mum, and working full time, when did she even have the time for an affair when Harry knew her every move.

One day whilst out, Anita was lunching with the girls and Christina and her friends, Harry rang Anita to see where she was. At this point they had all had lunch and were looking around town in the clothes shops. Anita told Harry where she was and he demanded that she came home right at that minute. There was a problem with Anita's phone and she had to put it onto loud speaker to hear Harry, she told him no he would have to wait until they had finished shopping. Unbeknown to Harry ,everyone could hear what he was saying to Anita and he said 'Right I'll come and drag you home then you fucking, cunting whore.'

Anita's friends could not believe what they had all just heard and Louise said 'You are not going home to that,' and took Anita and Christina home with her in a taxi. Anita switched off her phone; Louise went and picked up Charlie while Harry was out. Anita stayed at her friends for a couple of days whilst deciding what to do and in the meantime had no contact with Harry. Anita spent most of her time crying, she was so scared. Although she had known for such a long time her marriage was well and truly over, it was still hard to walk away. Louise took Anita home after a few days to get some things. Harry has let the tyres down on her car so she couldn't drive it away. Anita was shaking whilst walking up to the front door and was scared to go in. When she walked in Harry started crying and held on to Anita, begging her not to leave him and said he would get help and change, and that if she left him he would kill himself, so once again guilt, with emotional blackmail, took over and won. Anita put on a brave face and tried to give her marriage yet another chance.

The stress started to affect Anita's health, feeling unwell and with constant bad headaches lasting for hours. Anita went to the doctors and he diagnosed high blood pressure and monitored Anita for forty-eight hours as it was so high and put Anita on medication to lower it. Not long after this, Anita's vision began blurring a lot. Anita went to the opticians, who recommended a cat scan. The conclusion was that it was migraine related and Anita was put on more medication. Anita's blood pressure wasn't settling so she was put on even more medication to help, which appeared to work most of the time. However, Anita was monitored regularly and was told she would be on it for the rest of her life.

One night Harry went out with his work friends and invited Anita along. Anita was on shift so could not go, although Harry already knew this. Harry asked Anita to pick him up when she finished her shift. When Anita's shift finished, she rang Harry and he had switched his phone off, so Anita randomly rang till he switched it back on. When Harry answered, he told Anita he would come home when he was good and ready and not before. Anita told him she needed to be up early and wouldn't wait up all night. Then Anita noticed a bottle of wine missing. Annabelle had given it to her as a present, so she rang Harry to see where it was. He had given it to his friend as a present. Anita told him he had no right to do that and told him to go fuck himself and she wanted a divorce anyway and then she went to bed. About an hour later Harry got home and was mad, he woke Anita up by shouting at her and grabbing her by the hair and constantly banged Anita's head on the post on the end of the bed, calling her a whore and a slut. Anita was so scared she couldn't fight him off, he was too strong and she didn't stand a chance. When Harry finally stopped, he just crashed out and went to sleep. Anita, by this time, had to be up for work in a couple of hours, so she went downstairs and had a cup of tea. No way was she staying in the bed with Harry.

Anita then went and had a bath and stayed awake. Her head was hurting so much, the pain was excruciating and her vision was blurring. Anita did not even have any tears left inside her and just felt empty and in shock. Anita knew there was no way that she could drive to work that morning so rang for a taxi. When Anita arrived at work, her friend, Kev, thought Anita had been out on the town as she looked rough. Anita told him she just felt ill and couldn't drive in. Kev said she should have rung in sick. As it was Harry's day off she was not going to spend the day at home with him. Kev went home and Jason arrived at work. Jason told Anita she looked ill, Anita told him she felt ill but wanted to be at work. Jason tried to arrange cover for her to let her go home, but as luck would have it, no one could cover. Jason was great and told her to just chill and watch television and made her tea and toast and told her to just be there as an extra for emergency, unbeknown to him she was happy to stay at work. When Anita did go home that evening, she went straight to bed after walking the dog. Harry just stood in the doorway staring at Anita not saying anything and the dog kept growling at him, so she let the dog sleep on the bed with her.

Chapter 10

Please God

The next morning, Harry got up and went to work. Anita stayed in bed till lunch time then took Charlie the dog to the beach and once again just prayed to God 'Please let Mark come and find me and still love me, I don't think I can go on much longer. I feel like I'm slowly dying,' then carried on walking her beloved dog along the beach and telling him all her woes.

Weeks had passed and Harry was getting ready to go out with his friends. Anita decided to have a bottle of wine, which made her either very stupid or brave and rang Harry telling him she could not cope anymore and wanted a divorce. Anita soon sozzled her wine and got through the rest of the bottle. She didn't care anymore and went to bed and fell asleep.

When Harry got in, he went running up the stairs punched Anita in the face and then put his hands around her throat, then hitting her in the head constantly. Anita said 'No more, you are killing me, please no more,' and started crying. Then Harry grabbed her hair and dragged Anita to the stairs and pushed her backwards over the banisters holding onto her legs. Harry told her she was pathetic and he'd wasted the best years of his life with her. Anita thought this is it, he's going to kill me and tried to pull herself up, but she couldn't, terror just filled her body. She didn't want to die like this but thought she might as well give in, after all she felt like she was slowly dying inside anyway. This would be all over and there would be no more feeling scared or worry any more. Then Harry stopped and pulled her up and called her a 'Stupid fucking bitch.'

At work a couple of days later, one of the staff asked Anita 'What's happened to you?'

Anita lied and said 'I fell down the stairs,' although her attempts at trying to cover up the bruising to her face didn't work.

Mick said 'Don't lie to me; someone's done that to you.'

Anita could feel the tears running down her face and said to Mick 'I can't talk about it, don't tell anyone,' then pulled herself together and got on with work. At break time Mick offered to sort Harry out. Anita told Mick not to get involved and she would sort it out when she was ready. So Mick left well alone, although he did tell Lissie. So Lissie told her to leave Harry before she was carried out in a box. When Anita got home that evening she just carried on as if nothing had happened and walked Charlie on the beach.

A week later it was Anita and Harry's wedding anniversary and they went to Spain for the week. Anita just got bladdered all the time and was asleep by tea time, leaving Harry in the hotel with other guests they had talked to. These people were going back to Spain in a couple of months and asked Harry and Anita to join them and so they booked to return.

When they returned home, Anita got a phone call from Tracey telling her that her ex key-child had died. Anita broke down and cried hysterically, it was such a shock although Anita knew he was ill. Anita went down for the funeral a week later, with Tracey and Lea. Although such a sad time, it was great to see her friends who she missed so much. She also visited Fiona whilst there, as she missed her loads too.

Back home Anita had no support from Harry, not even asking how the funeral went or if she was alright. Anita just plodded on and went back to work. Christina was out a lot with her new boyfriend, staying at his flat. A couple of months soon passed. Harry and Anita flew back out to Spain meeting up with the friends they met there before. Anita did have a good time chilling by the pool and Harry seemed chilled and was being exceptionally nice to Anita. Whilst there, Anita received a phone call from her sister, which was very unusual as her sister knew they were in Spain. Anita thought something must be wrong. Diane said 'Are you sitting down?

Anita replied 'Yes why, what's wrong?

'Diane said 'You are going to be a nan. Christina is pregnant.'

Anita told Harry, who appeared to be in shock and not happy one bit, Anita was really pleased and spoke to Christina asking her why she didn't tell her. Christina thought she would be disappointed with her. Anita told her not to be silly as it was her life and as long as she was happy it was fine. The news that she had a grandchild to look forward to was the best thing to happen for ages.

After a few weeks being back home, things appeared really settled and Anita was happy buying bits for her grandchild's arrival, which would be just before Christmas. Coming in from shopping one day, Harry was running up the stairs with a petrol can, Anita said to him 'What are you doing?'

He replied 'Torching the house with you in it.'

Immediately fear came over Anita, a few weeks to her fortieth birthday and she wouldn't be here to see her grandchild arrive. Anita thought for a minute 'No way is he doing this to me,' and just ran up the stairs, chasing him and struggling to get the petrol can off him. Christina came in the front door and when she realised what was going on, shouted at Harry, telling him to stop it and stop being so stupid. Harry just stopped, he didn't speak to anyone for days. Christina stayed at her boyfriend's even more often.

Louise rang a few days later asking Anita if she wanted to go on a girl's night out with them. Whilst out, Anita got a phone call from Harry's friend saying that he was pissed and asked if he should take him home or did she want to come and get him. Anita said to just take him home and put him on the sofa and let him sleep it off and then forgot about it. When walking home with the girls, as they had all decided to get taxis from Anita's. They saw Harry standing in the front garden looking mad, then he went back into the house. Christina was right behind Anita as he lunged at her. Christina pushed Anita out of the way and punched Harry in the mouth and said 'Don't you dare hit my mum.' Harry was shocked at this and one of the neighbours called the police who seemed to appear within seconds. Harry started shouting at the police and swearing at them, so they arrested him and put him in the cells for the night. When they took him away, Anita went into the kitchen. The kitchen floor was covered in glass. Harry had drunk all the alcohol in the house then smashed all the bottles on the floor. Anita soon cleaned this mess up with help from her friends, then went and stopped at Diane's for the night.

Harry was mad with Anita the next day for not trying to get him out of the cells, although it was all his own doing. What could she have done anyway, there was just no reasoning with him.

Anita felt like she was losing her mind at times and she noticed that when she went out with Harry, she would be completely drunk, though drinking the same amount as when out with Christina or any of her friends. Anita began to suspect Harry of spiking her drinks as she would just black out. Anita told Fiona her thoughts and they decided, at some point when Fiona was up visiting, to swop drinks and see if Fiona blacked out. Returning home one night, Anita stripped into her underwear to go to bed as she was too hot to put bed clothes on and wouldn't sleep without anything on, in the night she needed a wee so made it to the toilet, but being so tired didn't make it back to her room and fell asleep on the bathroom floor. Next thing, Lee, Christina's boyfriend shouted to Christina to come get her mum to bed as he had found her asleep in her underwear on the bathroom floor. Much to the amusement of everyone the following morning.

Chapter 11

Birthday celebrations

Wow, how time flies by Anita thought, her fortieth birthday was now here, relatives were over and Anita was out for lunch with her friends in the noodle bar in town. They downed quite an amount of wine between them and were, to say the least, very merry.

Christina and lee came to walk Anita home and put her to bed for a couple of hours, to sleep it off before going out that evening. Christina ran a bath for Anita then woke her up while guests were arriving. Anita was in the bathroom for a long time, Christina went up and checked on Anita and found her naked, covered in talc and painting her toe nails, she just laughed at her mum and said 'Hurry up mum, everyone's waiting for you'.

Anita soon got dressed in a belly dancing outfit as they were all in fancy dress. When she went downstairs, lots of her friends and relatives were there and her friends clubbed together to buy her a watch with diamantes in it, as they knew how much she loved sparkly things.

That evening went really well, Anita was up dancing with everyone till 3am.

The months rolled on and Christina gave birth before Christmas. Anita and Harry were over the moon and this little person seemed to bring them closer together again. How long it would last didn't bother Anita, just at this moment in time her family seemed happy. Anita helped out a lot with her grandchild whenever she could and spent a lot of time with Christina and Lee, even volunteering to babysit if they went to the supermarket or out anywhere. Anita absolutely loved having her grandchild, it seemed to give her a purpose in life, and she loved this little person so much. Even Harry appeared to be mellowing.

A couple of months after Christmas, Harry got a phone call from his sister saying his mother was dying. Harry got on the train but didn't make it. She died before he arrived. Harry stayed down with his family for the week. Then Anita, Christina and Lee joined them the day before the funeral. Whilst getting ready, Lucy rang Anita, saying she had been trying to get hold of her as she thought someone had told Anita then realised they hadn't. Anita said 'What about.'

Lucy took a minute and said 'Tracey died.' Anita just broke down then and there, an hour before her mother-in-law's funeral. She had been told one of her best friends had died. Anita rang Fiona and Lea, sobbing on the phone, she arranged to go home after her mother-in-law's funeral, and come back down on the coach for Tracey's funeral two days later.

At her mother-in-law's funeral, the church was packed out and Anita, already teary eyed before arriving, stayed to support Harry and put on a brave face, it was her mother-in-law after all. They all returned home the next day. Anita got the night coach back down south ready for Tracey's funeral. Lea picked Anita up and they went together. The funeral was so sad, especially seeing Tracey's children left behind and people fighting over custody of them. When the coffin went down, to Rod Stewart's 'Have I told you lately', Anita bawled her eyes out. Tracey was crazy over Rod Stewart, although all Anita's life she was not the slightest bit interested in him, now she found herself listening to his music. It reminded her of Tracey and the good times they had together.

It was soon time to go back home. On arrival, Harry was waiting for Anita with a present. Anita opened it, it was a dildo. 'What do I want this for?' said Anita.

'I want you to use it and make me a film of yourself with it,' said Harry.

'No way am I doing that,' said Anita.

'Yes you will, I will kill you and then myself if you don't,' said Harry.

At that moment, Harry grabbed Anita's hair and told her to get upstairs and do it now. Anita, trembling with fear, went upstairs with Harry still holding onto her hair, and walked into the bedroom. He pushed Anita to the floor and told her to get on her knees; she did as she was told. He undid his jeans and pulled down his pants. He had not showered for days and the odour was foul, he then forced his penis into her mouth and told her to suck and do it fucking properly. Anita wanted to curl up and cry and fought back the tears and the need to vomit. When it was over, Anita was disgusted at the thought. The fear of Harry was so much in her head. She, later that day, drank two bottles of wine and did some films for Harry to shut him up, feeling so disgusted with herself, she felt sickened and hated herself and just knew she had to get away but was just not strong enough. Anita went out the next weekend with Harry and some friends and, having too much to drink, she fell asleep on the dog bed. Harry started to kick her and only stopped when one of their friends came in and saw him doing it and told him to leave her alone.

Anita was oblivious to this till the next morning when she felt bruised and the friend told her what happened. So there was Anita trying so hard to try and save this marriage against her better judgement and Harry obviously did not seem to care at all.

Despite all this, Anita carried on and told Harry she felt like she was slowly dying inside and could not get rid of this feeling however much she tried. Anita made excuses to try not to be intimate with Harry unless under the influence of alcohol, as his touch made her skin crawl and his hygiene was somewhat to be desired most of the time. He did not even shower before getting into bed, after doing manual building work and was covered in dust and dirt and smelled of body odour. He then expected Anita to be intimate with him. If she didn't, he would smash things up and accuse her of sleeping around or hold her against her will and take what he wanted anyway. A lot of the time, like before, Anita gave in rather than have the hassle of being scared or hurt.

Chapter 12

Would you tell him?

Anita's mum rang her one afternoon, to see how she was and told her she was going to Canada to see Aunt Floss and would Anita like to go with her. Anita said she would love to, but Harry wouldn't let her go without him. So they decided to book the holiday and not tell him until the time, saying Aunt Floss wasn't too well and mum had to go and see her and didn't want to travel on her own. Giving Harry no notice to be able to arrange to go himself.

Anita felt bad lying but so needed to get away from him before she went out of her mind. Whilst out in Canada, Anita put on a brave face and let everyone think things were ok between her and Harry, as she was too embarrassed to say otherwise. Anita had a great time with her cousins in Canada. It was so relaxing not having to worry about anything back home, she just put it to the back of her mind. Remembering the last time she was in Canada, she was dating Mark and wished so much she was till with him.

Anita went up into the Rocky Mountains for a couple of days with cousin Derek and his wife to be. Mum, Aunt Floss and the cat, Bill, who they kept on a lead when outside the trailer. There were such beautiful views in the mountains and it was so relaxing,. Anita wished she could stay there forever with nothing to worry about. After being up in the mountains for the weekend, they all went to cousin Katy's and spent a couple of nights there with her and her family and had a day out at a little town called Dead Man's Land. Anita and Katy had such a laugh that day, on the way back to Katy's, they got a puncture in the car and Anita said jokingly 'It's like a horror film, they are trying to keep us in their town.' Which made them laugh even more. Driving along with a puncture they saw a Go Karting place and pulled in there. Katy said Anita had to ask them to pump the tyre up for them as Canadians love the English accent. They sure did, so Anita, Katy and the children headed home again.

Time flew by, and soon they had to return home. Anita missed her daughter and granddaughter terribly and was ready to go home to them. She was apprehensive about returning home although she was pleased to be seeing Christina and her granddaughter. She did not want to be home.

Not long after her return, the accusations soon started again and Anita was thinking 'I might as well have been having an affair, then I could understand it.' Life carried on regardless. Anita still lunched with her friends, whatever Harry had to say.

Christina and Lee decided to get married and invited lots of family and friends. Fiona came too, and Christina sat her with Anita's good friends, Marty and Anthony. Fiona thought they were fabulous as it was the first time she had met them although she said Anita often spoke about them fondly.

As Christina walked down the aisle, Anita fought hard to hold back the tears. Here was her beautiful daughter getting married and so happy. Anita was so pleased for them both. The wedding went really well, it was a wonderful day. A couple of days later they set off for their honeymoon to Australia, with Anita and Mum looking after her granddaughter. Anita thought how great this was. When in

Australia they had such a great time going round the wildlife parks, whilst Christina and Lee went and did their own thing for a week. It was great; Anita loved having that time with her mum and her granddaughter and visiting relatives and relaxing in the hot tub with a Bacardi and coke and chilling on the beach. One day they all went out on a boat with Christina and Lee to see the dolphins, it was such an amazing experience with the dolphins coming right up to the boat. As always, time flew by and soon it was time to return home.

One night Anita was sitting in bed watching television and Harry came in. He turned around to her and said 'I've got a gun, if you ever try to leave me, I will shoot you. You cannot hide anywhere from me, I will find you and get you, if you ever go with anyone else I will shot them too.' After that Anita just curled up and tried to go to sleep whilst Harry just stood there in the doorway staring at her and not speaking in the dark.

At this time in her life, Anita was feeling very mixed emotions and just did not know which way to turn but knew somehow, some way, she had to get away from Harry. Anita noticed that Harry had been going into the loft a lot, so decided to do some investigating when Harry went to work. She waited until she heard his motorbike drive away and got the ladders and went up into the loft to see what Harry's attraction was up there. She could not believe what she was seeing and thought 'This must be a joke.' Right in front of her was a monitor showing her bedroom, all this time Harry had been filming Anita in the house whilst he was out at work. Anita waited for him to get home that evening and confronted Harry. He admitted it, saying he was checking to see if she brought anyone home, who she was seeing.

Anita told Harry he was out of his mind; he replied that it was all her fault he was like this.

A couple of weeks passed, things appeared to calm down. Harry got up and went to work, or so Anita thought, even hearing his motorbike drive away. Anita lay in bed for a couple of hours longer as she hadn't been sleeping well, then got up and ran a bath. Relaxing in the bath for about ten minutes. Harry shouted 'BOO,' frightening the life out of Anita. He had been hiding under the bed, parked his motorbike around the back and sneaked back into the house to see what Anita was up to, so he could catch her.

Anita was getting really freaked out by Harry's behaviour and went to see the doctor about it. The doctor said, unless Harry did anything else bizarre or hurt himself or Anita, only then would Anita be able to apply to section him under the mental health act.

Anita didn't tell Harry that she had been to see the doctor about him and only told Fiona and Lea as she was getting more scared by the minute. She still shrugged it off and tried to carry on as usual. Anita booked a holiday to Spain and invited some friends who wanted to go too, so ended up being seven of them all going. When they arrived in Spain, Harry was all over their friends, groping the women even in front of Anita and making sexual innuendoes towards them, and when walking along the street sight-seeing, he would put his arm around anyone but Anita. Acting as if she was not even there with him, being completely disrespectful towards her. This obviously made the friends feel uncomfortable. All Anita did was try so hard to make this marriage work, although she didn't even want to be in the same room as Harry anymore and all he did was throw it back in her face. Anita, in turn, didn't care anymore now and thought 'Fuck him, if he kills me, he kills me; all I care about is Christina and my granddaughter.'

Anita's mum needed more hospital treatment and another operation, so Anita was back and forth once again. Anita's friend Linsay had moved to London, so whilst down there Anita had arranged to meet Linsay for lunch before returning home on the coach. When Anita arrived back home that evening, Harry insisted on smelling Anita's breath, accusing her of having lesbian sex in the toilets at the coach station, then pulled Anita back by her hair, Anita tried to run to the front door, Harry pulled her, whacked her head on the front door, then pushed her against the wall and put his hands around her throat and squeezed tight, strangling her.

Anita felt her life momentarily blank out, when coming round Anita just stood in fear, shaking with tears running down her face and was just so scared. Harry actually came close to killing her.

How Anita survived this she did not know. She obviously had much more will to live and survive in her, than she thought.

Anita had work the next day and tried to cover up the bruising around her neck with a scarf, although the weather was very warm as it was early June. Anita just pretended she must have been coming down with something and felt chilly, except at work, Kev noticed the bruising around her neck when the scarf slipped. Anita just broke down at that point and told Kev everything and how scared she was now for her life, and that she knew she had to get out of there but had to do it at the right moment. Anita had arranged with Kev to ring or text him any time of the day or night, not even having to say anything, just for him to ring 999 for her.

Anita then confided more in Christina about what was happening as well just in case. As Anita found it hard to turn her head side to side and the bruising from the strangulation caused her to have a dry cough for a while, she thought it best to let her know. Kev had confided in Woody, who Anita also got on well with, what Anita had disclosed to him, and between them they kept a watch over Anita to generally check if she was ok. They tried to cheer her up if they noticed she looked down. Kev told Anita he let Woody know so if she needed to chat and he wasn't about, Woody was there also. Anita found strength in this, knowing that they were there for her.

Chapter 13
Don't underestimate the power of prayers

Anita once again tried to carry on as normal, planning what to do and when to get away, all confused as she was no longer sleeping or eating properly.

One day whilst chatting to Aunt Floss online, Sheila, Mark's sister popped up on an online chat. Anita hadn't spoken to Sheila for years. Sheila told Anita that she was going to Mark's for a barbecue for his birthday, and Anita asked Sheila to wish Mark a happy birthday from her. She thought no more about it, as she and Mark hadn't spoken since she left him and she thought he wouldn't want to know. Anita gave Sheila her phone number to meet up for coffee next time when she was heading south. About a month later, Anita got a text message from a number she didn't recognise saying 'Thanks for the birthday wishes, how are you?'

Anita replied to this saying 'Who are you?'

Then got a message back saying 'Go back 25 years.'

Immediately Anita knew it was Mark and texted him back, asking how he had got her number. Mark said Sheila had given it to him. He said he just wondered how she was. Anita told him that she was married and was good and didn't mention all the bad things that had happened. Mark told her that sometimes he drove up north with his work and could he stop by for a brew and see her and meet her husband, Anita said yes straight away, and Mark said 'I bet you are still as beautiful as you were at eighteen,'

Anita said 'Lol.'

When Harry arrived home from work that day, Anita told him that Mark had been in touch. Harry was not happy with this at all and said 'No way is he coming here.' So Anita just left it. A couple of weeks later, it was Anita's mum's birthday, so Anita took her for lunch with Tom. That evening, Anita and her Mum went to a barbecue with Fiona just along the road. When Anita arrived home, she went for an appointment at her hairdresser's. She hadn't spoken to Christina that morning. After the hair dryer had finished, Anita noticed she had several missed calls from Christina, so she rang her. Christina said 'Thank God you are ok; I thought Dad had done you in.' This comment really hit Anita hard.

When Anita arrived home, Harry accused her of seeing someone down south. Anita's reply was 'Yeah right,' she'd just had enough and knew it was time to leave.

Anita's mum had another hospital appointment and Anita really did not want to return back home this time, but carried on. Whilst at her mum's, Anita visited some of her friends and told them she was planning to leave Harry and, although scared, felt stronger in herself. Anita was also texting her friend, Marie, back home, whilst at her mum's, just silly girl talk, pretending to run away together. When Anita returned home once again, unbeknown to her, Harry went through her phone, reading her messages. He then accused her of having an affair with Marie, and smashed up the bedroom, Anita knew it was time to leave.

Anita got up early the next morning and went to work as usual and when someone asked her if she was ok, Anita started crying hysterically and the whole lot came out. Anita's friends at work, could not believe what they were hearing. Anita had been going through this and putting on a brave face and no one knew.

Maggie was great, she sent Anita and Marie out to calm down and get things sorted.

Anita went to the doctor's and she signed Anita off work. Anita moved in with Christina for the time being. Anita had left Harry a letter when she left, telling him she could not take the abuse anymore and detailed some of the things that he had done to her and also told him that she wanted a divorce, that there was no going back this time. She told him that she had tried so hard in this marriage only to have him completely disrespect her at every opportunity. Harry came round to Christina's apologising and said that he knew that it was all his own doing and begged Anita to give him another chance. Anita stayed strong and told him 'No, not this time, I cannot do it anymore, you are making me ill.' Harry appeared to remain calm at this and went back home with tears in his eyes.

Harry made several visits to Christina's at this time, so Anita tried her best to stay out of his way, even if it meant popping round to Diane's till he went back home, just to keep away from him. She really did not want to be in his company and thought about getting a divorce on the grounds of domestic abuse. She was worried, although the doctor knew what had been happening and a couple of her friends. It was still her word against his. Was she strong enough to stand up in court in front of him, although she knew she should, she had already taken the first step and walked away from the domestic abuse before it killed her.

About a month had passed, Anita texted Mark and told him she was coming down to her mum's for a Christmas visit. Mark asked if he could take her out for lunch. Anita didn't believe what she was hearing, all these years regretting leaving Mark and praying for him to come and find her, and here he was. Anita confided in her friends and just went for it, to meet Mark when she went south for Christmas.

Anita was so nervous, feeling like a teenager all over again, with her stomach doing somersaults just at the thought of meeting Mark. Anita kept saying to her mum and Fiona 'Do I look alright? making them laugh. When Mark arrived they just hugged each other for what seemed like forever to Anita. They had lunch and they both talked for hours. Anita could not take her eyes off Mark and could not believe he was actually here with her. Being back in Mark's presence, the empty space in Anita's life just faded away and she felt complete. It was time for Mark to go back to work and he asked Anita if he could see her again the next day and cook her dinner. Anita said yes, as she did not want to leave Mark's side. Mark took Anita back to her mum's and said goodbye, they hugged each other for ages.

At Mark's home the next evening, Mark poured Anita wine, so Anita stayed over so as not to drink and drive. Mark offered to sleep on the sofa and let Anita have his bed. After dinner, Anita and Mark went up to his room so they could have some privacy as Mark house shared with a friend and they had a house full of visitors. Mark and Anita sat on the bed watching television and snuggling up to each other. Mark asked Anita if he could kiss her, then Anita sat up nervously and kissed him. Mark moved back and asked Anita 'Is this really what you want? Me.'

'Yes,' replied Anita.

Mark said 'I've loved and missed you all my life.'

Anita told Mark that she loved and had missed him for so long, and couldn't believe that they were there together again after all these years. They never went back downstairs that night and woke up, snuggled up together, the next morning, it was mind blowing. This was now the start of a new chapter in her life.

Chapter 14

New year, new life

It was New Years Eve and Anita was working till late. She had planned to go straight to bed when she got home at Christina's, she had moved in with her and Lee. Christina and Lee went out to a party as Anita arrived home, leaving Anita looking after her granddaughter. No sooner had Anita got her pyjama's on when there was a knock at the door. Anita called through. It was Harry. Anita shouted out 'I'm going to bed, what do you want?'

Harry said 'I want some milk the shop's shut. Anita went and got some milk and took it to the door and gave it to Harry. As she went to shut the door Harry put his foot in the doorway and said 'Let me come in and just talk to you.'

'No,' said Anita. 'I've got to be up early, you are not coming in, leave me alone, goodnight,' and shoved the door so hard, Harry moved his foot and went away.

As midnight struck, Anita's phone rang, it was Mark, he had been to a party and was a little drunk and saying 'I love you my baby, please don't ever leave me again, hurry up and get here with me, I've got to go to sleep now, I love you so much.'

'I love you too, cannot wait to get there,' said Anita.

Anita was up early the next day, New Year's day, ready for a long drive down south to be with Mark for a couple of nights and also visit mum. It was six o'clock in the morning and Anita set off in the car for the long journey down south to Mark's, finally arriving just before eleven as it had been a good drive. Mark answered the door and flung his arms around Anita.

Anita was tired after the long drive, so snuggled up to Mark on the sofa and fell asleep for an hour with Mark waking her up to get ready to go to his brother Gordy's for dinner and meet Gordy's wife Candy. Mark told Anita that she would love Candy and get on well with her.

As they arrived, Gordy and Candy welcomed Anita. Anita felt at ease with them straight away and got on really well with them. After dinner it was time to go round to Mark's mum. Anita was a little worried at this as she had not seen her for years.

Arriving at Mark's mum's, mum gave Anita a big hug and said 'Please don't ever break my sons' heart ever again.'
Anita replied 'I won't ever leave him again, I missed him too much.' Then pops got up and made everyone a cup of tea and they all chatted for a while before setting off to Mark's sister Sheila's. It was nice to see Sheila again. Anita was really happy that Mark's family had welcomed her back so lovingly and that she felt comfortable around them straight away.

Then next day Anita went to visit her own mum for the day while Mark was at work. Anita arrived back at Mark's just as he was getting in from work. Mark's house mate, Scotty, was in with his girlfriend Tina. Mark cooked dinner for everyone then Mark and Anita chilled out and fell asleep early as both had to get up early the next day, Mark had work and Anita had to drive back home. Anita hated having to leave Mark to return home, it was tearing her apart. She wanted to stay forever but had to be realistic with them both working and so far apart. As Anita arrived home her phone was already ringing. It was Mark, as Anita answered

Mark said 'Hello my lover,' Anita giggled at this, then Mark told her his brother had rung him to say that his father had passed away that day.

Anita's heart sank, here she was three hundred miles away from Mark and she could not be there to comfort him. 'I wish I was there with you, I hate being so far away, especially now, as I cannot even cuddle you,' said Anita.

'I wish you were here too babe, I need you so much, I love you,' said Mark.

'Love you too,' said Anita.

Anita and Mark rang each other several times a day, missing each other terribly. Two weeks later, Anita drove back down to Mark's and they set off to Southampton to go across to the Isle Of Wight with the rest of the family, to go to Mark's father's funeral. After the cremation, the wake was at a pub in Shanklin, where everyone had dinner and drinks and remembered old times. Although it was a sad time, it was good for Anita to be with all Mark's family, all together, and see Arron and Kimmy again with their children all grown up, and meet up with Shane and his wife Lily. After the wake, they set back off to the ferry port to return home to Mark's. Anita drove as Mark had been drinking, and he was telling Anita which way to go and how to drive, while being very giggly. They arrived home and Mark fell asleep, so Anita snuggled up to him and went to sleep having to get up early the next morning to return home for work.

When back home, Anita went house hunting as she knew she couldn't live with Christina forever. Louise said that Anita could move in with her and her boyfriend Dan, but Anita did not want to put herself on anyone and be a burden. In the meantime Anita and Mark were travelling to be with each other and it was so tiring but they could not bear to be away from each other.

Mum had another hospital appointment, so Anita went down to mum's and took her to her appointment. Later that day, Anita went to Mark's, as she arrived Mark came to meet her outside and said 'I've got someone to meet you, my son Dean.'

Anita was worried at this although she knew it had to happen but was still worried in case Dean didn't like her. She had nothing to worry about as they got on well from the start. Mark was estranged from his daughters, Susie and Belle, and did not know how to go about rectifying the situation. Dean had twin sisters which were Mark's stepdaughters and Mark took Anita to meet them and they both appeared to be ok with Anita and lovely. Anita had a lovely weekend visiting with Mark but as usual had to return home for work.

Soon Anita was due to go on holiday with Mum, to the Dominican Republic for cousin Derek, from Canada's, wedding. There were quite a few people going, friends and family and all meeting up and staying at the same hotel.

Anita did not want to go without Mark and Mark wanted to go, so she booked for Mark to go as well. They were excited about going and went holiday clothes shopping together. The holiday was soon upon them. Anita drove down to mum's and stayed with Mum overnight, then drove to Mark's early in the morning to pick Mark up. On the flight they all fell asleep for a while.

Chapter 15

Dominican Republic

Touch down, Dominican Republic, the heat was stifling but great. The rep was there already waiting to meet them to take them to their five star, all inclusive, hotel, that they were all booked into with the wedding party. When they arrived at the hotel, which was an absolutely huge complex and beautiful, they all checked in and were taken to their apartments. As they walked in, Anita realised that they had to share the same bedroom as Mum, so they tried to get an extra room but they couldn't as the hotel was fully booked. 'Oh well,' Anita said. 'We will just have to get on with it.'

Mum, Anita and Mark were on their own for a couple of days before everyone else arrived, so went out sunbathing and cooling down in the pool, which had a bar in the middle of it, which was very convenient. After a couple of days relaxing and chilling out by themselves, Aunt Floss arrived with her new fella as she and Uncle Bob had divorced a while back. It was great to see Aunt Floss and good for Mum to catch up with her sister. Cousin Derek and wife to be, Hils, also arrived and lots of their friends, it was great to see everyone. Later that day, cousin Frank was arriving with his wife Toni and daughter Issy. As Frank stepped off the transfer bus, he saw Mark, Mark and Frank ran to each other having a big hug as they had not seen each other for years, they had so much to catch up on. That evening everyone met up in the restaurant for dinner and it was great all chatting and eating together with the alcohol flowing freely.

This was the life. They all spent their days meeting up at the pool sunbathing and chilling out together, waiting for the big day to arrive. The day before the wedding, Uncle Bob arrived with his new wife, it was good to see Uncle Bob again and meet his wife. They didn't join everyone in the evening for dinner, they decided to do their own thing. The morning of the wedding, Anita and Mum had booked into the hairdresser's and had their hair pinned up so it looked perfect. The guests all went down to the beach and sat in the chairs all set up, then the music played and everyone looked around to see the beautiful bride walking down the beach with Issy scattering petals before her and Cousin Derek standing at the ceremony tower with a huge smile on his face looking at his beautiful bride. The wedding day was amazing, everyone had a brilliant time. At the end of the day, Mark and Anita walked Mum back to the apartment and went back out to meet some of the others to carry on with the evening with drinking games. When Mark and Anita finally decided to go back to the apartment that evening, they were getting frustrated at having to share a bedroom with Mum and ended up making love on the stairwell before going into the apartment.

When they went into the apartment Mum was asleep, Mark and Anita went onto the balcony and shut the door and made love again on the balcony before going back in and getting into bed. Early in the morning there was a clinking of cups, Mum was making tea, waiting for Anita and Mark to get up. Anita and Mark went and showered together and made love in the shower before going down to the restaurant for breakfast with Mum. When they were all at the breakfast table, with Aunt Floss and her boyfriend, and some others, Mum said to everyone that when she woke up Mark had kicked the cover off himself in his sleep and that Mark had a piercing in his penis, everyone thought this was funny especially Mum. Mark wasn't bothered, just a little embarrassed that Mum had seen it though. Mark and Anita got up to go to the shop. Aunt Floss shouted out 'We know where you are going, you are going to have sex, while the apartment's empty,' everyone laughed. Mark and Anita went to the shop and then went to see what excursions were available. They booked on a dune buggy tour for the next day. Later they went back to look at the excursions which Mum and Aunt Floss had booked, an excursion to tour through the villages and go up the mountain to where the coco beans are picked and processed.

The next morning, Mark and Anita went for breakfast with Mum and everyone, then set off to the tour office and went on a truck with some others to get to the dune buggy centre. Anita sat in a buggy with Mark as she did not want to drive it, and they followed the guide with everyone else through the towns and then stopping in a little village where food and drink was laid on for them all before setting off back to the centre, it was thrilling driving along, crazy over the bumps and dirt track sandy roads. Anita and Mark had a great day.

As soon as they arrived back at the hotel, they went straight to the apartment to shower as they were so dirty, and once again made love in the shower before going down to the pool where the rest of the wedding party were, including Mum.

The next day after breakfast, Mark, Anita, Mum, Aunt Floss and her boyfriend, cousin Derek and Hils went on the village tour. It was a very bumpy ride up and down the rickety roads in the heat and the tour guide supplying rum and coke for the journey, in which everyone indulged, before stopping at a little village where cigars were made and on sale. Mark brought himself some cigars to take back home. The next stop was at the coffee and coco bean place, a tour guide took them through and gave them a talk about the coffee beans and coco beans and taste testing them and then through to the shop so people could buy some if they wished. This was a long day in the heat, in the truck, with the bumpy rickety ride, and Anita was glad to get back to the hotel to shower with Mark. Mark and Anita went to a different restaurant from the others that night, just to have some alone time, as there were five different restaurants at the hotel. Then met up with everyone afterwards. Cousin Derek asked Mark if he would like to go on a fishing trip the following day with the guys, so Anita arranged to do a shopping trip with Mum and Aunt Floss.

The next morning Anita felt lost without Mark as he was up so early to go fishing with the guys. Anita, Mum and Aunt Floss went for breakfast and set off round the shops and market stalls, most of the stalls had the same items as each other and the stall holders were all trying to get them to their stalls, it was like a cattle market. Anita thought she would just go back there with Mark another day.

That evening, before dinner time, Mark returned with the guys, they hadn't caught anything but had a great day and all seemed a little worse for wear, they had had plenty of alcohol on the boat and cannabis, of which Mark had brought a bag back with him to the hotel and shared it out to the guys there. Mark had some before getting in the pool and was paranoid that Mum knew he had been smoking it and as Mum walked past the pool, Mark ducked down in the pool as far as his eyes, just peeping over the water, looking like a hippo peeping. Anita and Hils laughed at him, Mum knew anyway as Aunt Floss had already told her.

It was soon time to go home and already packed and ready to go, the tour guide came and found them and said that their flight had been delayed and that he had already arranged it with the hotel for them all to stay another night in the same rooms, still all inclusive. Brilliant thought Anita ,another day in the sun, so Mum, Anita and Mark went and got into the pool and ready to spend another night with everyone. The next day they said their goodbyes to everyone and looked forward to when they could all meet up again.

Returning at Gatwick airport, it was cold and raining, a big difference to being in the Dominican Republic. Mark and Anita drove Mum home and Anita went back to Mark's till the weekend before returning home back up north. Anita hated leaving Mark, especially after spending three weeks with him and had tears rolling down her cheeks as they said their goodbyes. 'Love you baby' said Mark,

'Love you too' said Anita.

When Anita returned home to Christina's she was pining for Mark and rang him on arrival.

'Hello my baby,' said Mark.

'Hya my sexy man, I can't stand being away from you,' said Anita.

'Me too baby we will have to sort something out, would you move back down here?' said Mark.

'I can't be that far away from Christina,' said Anita.

'Ok baby, we will work it out, I love you so much,' Mark said.

'I love you too, I'll ring you tonight, I need to get my washing done, love you,' Anita said, and hung up.

Chapter 16

Marry me

Back at work, as work had to continue, Anita was toying with the idea whether to move back down south to be with Mark but knew she could not be that far away from Christina and just got on with things and put in extra hours at work. A couple of weeks went by just communicating with Mark on the phone every day, about ten times a day. Anita's phone rang, it was Mark, so she answered 'Hello my lover,' Mark said.

'Hya my gorgeous man, 'said Anita.

'I feel like a dirty old man, all I think about is you all day and I'm driving around with a hard on all day long, I even drove to the wrong part of London to my next job as you are on my mind all the time, I cannot concentrate on anything else,' said Mark. Anita giggled at this. 'Anyway baby, I'll call you later as I have to drive again now, bye bye baby I love you,' said Mark.

'Love you too' said Anita.

That weekend, Mark was coming up with Scotty who he house-shares with, to bring Mum's furniture up as Mum was moving up north and moving in with Diane. Anita could not wait for the weekend to come. Anita had also been flat hunting and found a flat to move into.

As the weekend arrived, Anita was so excited. Mark pulled up in his van outside, Anita ran out to greet him, throwing her arms around Mark and planting a kiss right on his lips. Scotty was sitting beside Mark and he had his dog with him. They got out of the van and came in and met Christina and Lee. They were only stopping for the night as Mark had to get back for work. Anita took Mark to view the flat; they had a lot of work to do in the flat but needed somewhere to live eventually. Then they went back to Christina's for dinner. Just after they finished dinner, Harry walked in. Mark being polite introduced himself to Harry. Harry didn't stop and went again. 'That went better than expected' said Anita to Mark.

A little while later, Anita, Mark and Scotty took the dogs for a walk along the promenade, it was chilly outside and the tide was in so they couldn't take the dogs on the beach. When they returned home to Christina's, they sat up chatting for a while before going to bed as Mark had an early start the next morning. The next morning, as Mark was leaving, he hugged Anita so tight saying 'I love you baby, I'll ring you when I get home.'

'Love you too,' said Anita.

Just as Mark had left, Harry walked up the road and he said to Anita that he thought about doing the brakes in on Mark's van so he doesn't make it home alive. 'That's nasty,' said Anita and went back inside with Harry following. Anita said to Christina, 'I'm just popping round Diane's, I'll see you later.'

'Ok Mum,' said Christina.

Anita stayed around Diane's for a while and returned just before going to bed so she didn't have to spend time with Harry; luckily he had gone before she got home.

A few weeks passed, with Anita and Mark travelling north and south to see each other. One day Mark had a delivery in Manchester, which was only an hour away from Anita, so he asked Anita if she would like to meet him for lunch as it was her day off., Anita loved the idea, she would get to see Mark instead of waiting another week because of the distance and them both working.

Anita got ready and drove to Manchester to meet Mark for lunch, as it was time to go, it was getting more and more difficult each time to say goodbye to each other and they clung on to each other for a while. 'Bye my baby, I love you so much,' said Mark.

'Bye, I love you too said Anita with tears falling down her face and Mark kissed the tears.

'Don't cry my baby, we'll be together soon' said Mark.

At work that weekend, they had a charity barbecue event to raise some money for people with brain injuries and Anita took Mum along. Anita brought some raffle tickets and won first prize, a five day away break in a hotel, with breakfast and evening dinner on the Isle of Man. Anita rang Mark to tell him and asked when he could get the time off and they could go together. They had arranged to go in June, hoping that the weather would be better. Anita drove Mum back to Diane's and the car was making a strange noise. Anita thought it was coming from the airbag. When she put the car in the garage, they said it was the brake pipe; it had a split in it. Dread went through Anita's head and asked them whether someone could have cut it. They said it was possible but hard to tell. Anita thought whether or not Harry had done it, as he did threaten to kill her if she was ever with anyone else. Anita put the thought to the back of her mind but it wouldn't go away. Harry did say about doing the brakes on Mark's van, maybe he did do it, but there is no way that she could prove it or that anyone would believe her at that, so just had to lay it to rest.

It was soon June, Anita and Mark were ready to go to the Isle of Man. Christina drove them to Liverpool docks to get the ferry across. It was chilly on the crossing but they soon arrived in Douglas and walked up the road to the Claremont Hotel. The hotel was a bit dated but the staff were all friendly and helpful. They soon settled into their room, then made love and had a shower before going down to the dining room for dinner. The next morning, they went down for breakfast and then out for the day, walking along the promenade in Douglas they came across a seat with a statue of Norman Wisdom on it, after a lot of walking that morning they decided to go and find a pub which had the England matches on and went and had lunch in there whilst watching the match. After the match, they went for another walk along the promenade, soon it was evening, the afternoon seemed to fly by. They went back to the hotel and had their evening dinner, the food was very good at the hotel and everything was very clean. After dinner they went up to their rooms to put some warmer clothes on before going back out. Mark said to Anita 'When you're my wife,'

Anita stopped him in his tracks. 'What? And what do you mean, when I'm your wife, you haven't asked me to marry you, you doughnut,' said Anita.

'Marry me, be my wife please, I love you so much, I don't ever want to lose you again, will you marry me? said Mark.

'Yes, of course I will marry you, I love you, I don't ever want to be apart from you again,' said Anita. They never left their room again that night.

The next morning Mark said 'Let's look for rings.' They ended up in a chocolate shop instead and decided to look for rings when they got back home. Mark wanted to set date for the wedding already and Anita told him we'll do that soon, and before that you need to rectify things with Susie and Belle, how, I don't know, but you have to do it, she told him. Mark knew this and it hurt him so much as it had caused him a lot of pain. They left the matter to rest until they returned home and carried on with their holiday. They decided to get the train around the island to see the views; they stopped off and had a pub lunch before getting back on the train fort the rest of the journey around the island. When they returned to Douglas, they had a long walk along the promenade before returning to the hotel for dinner, and had a drink in the hotel that evening. They decided to visit the museum in Douglas the next day and the castle ruins, amongst lots of walks along the promenade. The 5 days flew by.

Christina picked them up from Liverpool docks. Mark had to return home the next day to get back for work. When he returned home he rang Anita. 'Hello my baby, I've decided to move up in September, then I can give my boss plenty of notice to get someone else to replace me,' Mark said. Anita was so excited she couldn't wait for September to come.

Anita booked a week off work over her birthday to spend time with Mark, as Mark was working. She spent her birthday in the van with Mark and made them packed lunches for the day with two little bottles of Blossom Hill for herself and juice for Mark as he was driving. That evening, Mark took Anita out for dinner to a Chinese restaurant nearby. They had a lovely day together, Mark bought Anita a silver bracelet for her birthday with a little blue heart on it, and some earrings. Anita treasured her presents.

Chapter 17

Finally together

At the end of August Mark moved up, Anita was so happy. They stayed with Christina and Lee for a while before moving into the flat, as they had to wait for central heating to be put in and new windows and get the water sorted out. Woody came and helped, plumbing in the toilet for them. Even though the flat was a building site, they didn't care, as they were together at last, on their own forever. The only problem they had now was that Anita struggled with work, having to do the sleepovers, and work seemed to give her more and more sleepovers to do. She did not want to spend a night away from Mark especially now that they were living together.

'Babe,' said Mark, 'We need to set a date for our wedding.'

'Ok, how about June, not this one coming, the year after,' said Anita.

'That's too far away, I want to marry you now,' said Mark.

'We cannot afford it now, we have to save up, and look for somewhere first, also you need to get in touch with Susie and Belle first,' said Anita.

'How am I going to do that, other than going to their nan's and I don't want to see their mother ever again,' said Mark.

'Write a letter then, I'll help you,' said Anita. So they sat down together, Anita helped Mark to write a letter and posted it for him the next morning.

A few weeks passed and Mark got a phone call from Belle saying that she wanted to come up and see him and Susie was coming too with her daughters that Mark didn't even know about. Two granddaughters are what he had missed out on. After the phone call, Mark cried. He was so happy and had been scared all this time waiting for this day to come.

A couple of weeks later, the girls were arriving while Mark was at work. Anita was off so waited for them to arrive, Anita was worried about meeting them in case they did not like her. When they arrived, Anita went out to the car to meet them. They got on straight away as if they had known each other for years and Anita was at ease. They walked the dog to meet Mark from work and when Anita saw him coming out she told the girls, Susie pointed out granddad to her daughters, Shelley and Becky. Shelley went running up to granddad, shouting granddad and flung her arms around his legs. Mark was overwhelmed by this and fought back the tears and just hugged Susie and Belle.

Mark was so happy he had his girls back in his life and now marrying the woman that he had always loved. Now was the time to knuckle down and work hard to pay for the wedding but before that they had a festival to go to in the summer.

Anita had never been to a festival before, it was called Beatherder and it was near Clitheroe. A few friends from work were going and one was D Jing here. Anita got a free ticket on the condition that she worked in the perfumed garden whilst there, the vegetarian tent that had certain bands playing in there. All the friends camped together. Anita was the soberest person all weekend as she was working. It was a great weekend and very hot and what made it even better was that they got to see The Beat playing live. Mark was hoping that Bad Manners would be there too but they weren't. After this weekend, Mark and Anita went for all the overtime they could, to pay for the wedding. Anita's work's overtime had dried up, so she went to get a second job at a place she has briefly worked before. The boss, Robyn, was great and gave Anita the extra hours that she needed. Anita made a few new friends working there as well and had a good laugh with them as well as the dementia patients they were caring for, and got on really well and really enjoyed working there.

Susie and Belle came up for more visits and agreed to be bridesmaids at the wedding, Christina got on well with them as well, which was really good for Anita and Mark. Christina was a great help to Anita, helping out with the wedding and scouring the net for bargains and letting Anita know.

Anita and Mark decided they would like the pier for the wedding reception they went and booked it and wanted to put down a deposit to confirm. The pier booking person said not to pay yet, do it when they have arranged the food and everything they wanted and then pay a deposit. They were really happy with their choice and for transport Anita was going to have a horse and Cinderella carriage from along the promenade, she would book it on the day as it would save them a lot of money if Anita wasn't bothered about it being ribboned up for her wedding day. So the main things were organised. Christina went bridesmaid dress shopping with Anita and found some with seventy per cent off in the sales, which was really good for Anita and Mark considering they needed 5 of them as the twins were going to bridesmaids as well, and Dean one of the ushers, so none of the children were excluded. The grandchildren were to be flower girls and page boys. Christina had another daughter by this time and was due to drop another child 6 months before the wedding.

Work, work, work is all it seemed to be for a while before taking a weekend off for Pops' eightieth birthday. Pops by this time was very unsteady on his legs and needed a walking frame, Pops really wanted to get up and dance, as previously, back in the day, he had won trophies for ballroom dancing and he just loved to dance. Everyone was apprehensive of Pop's dancing now and were afraid that he would have a fall. Anita got Pops up and danced with him and everyone could see that he was so happy with a beaming smile on his face. So more guests got up and danced with him. The next morning Mark and Anita had to return home as they had to go back to work.

Time soon passed, it was 6 months to the wedding. Anita was ready to go pay for the reception at the pier, before she went to meet Mark from work so that they could go together, she got a phone call, she didn't get to it in time and it went on to her answerphone, it was the pier booking office, they had cancelled on her due to gay pride booking the same weekend, no surely not thought Anita, they must have known a long time ago and could have respectfully given her more notice, now she was in panic mode and needed to find somewhere quick so the invites to be sent.

Christina was on the case with Anita and Mark; eventually they found a hotel which was giving them an even better deal than the pier, La Parisienne, on the promenade, which was perfect. Anita and the bridesmaids were booked in the night before with the guests that were coming.

Finalising all the details 3 months before the wedding, Anita suddenly realised that she had not received her decree absolute through to the post from her divorce to Harry. So she phoned the court and they said that Harry hadn't done it. Raging with anger

Anita phoned Harry shouting at him, what more did he want, wasn't it enough that she agreed to say she was having an affair for him, to agree to let her have a divorce, as she thought it would have ran smoother than her taking him to court, spending thousands on divorcing him for domestic abuse. She gave Harry what for. Christina took Harry to the court to get it finalised and Anita received it just in time.

Another hiccup along the way, Mark spoke to the twins as they hadn't tried on their dresses so would have to make do. Then the twins wanted Harry to arrange transport for them to attend the wedding. Mark said 'No make your own way the same as Susie and Belle were doing.' Dean already had a lift with brother Gordy. The honeymoon was booked, they decided to go somewhere that neither of them had been before and decided on Kusadasi in Turkey. A five star, all inclusive hotel. Everything was ready, what else could go wrong? The stag do was sorted, the blokes were taking Mark to go watch Skaface band as Mark loved Ska music, he knew nothing about it. Christina, Belle and Susie had sorted out the hen night for Anita, even down to what she was wearing and she wasn't allowed to know until the night.

It was time for the stag do, the guys came and met Mark. Anita dropped them off at the venue where it was. Mark had a great night with the guys, coming home rather drunk and giggly with Frank and Ben, who stopped over. Cousin Tracy and her hubby Elli, and family arrived from Canada the next day, Anita and Christina collected them from the airport, it was great to see them. That night was the hen night. Anita arrived at Christina's with Susie and Belle and was given a 1980s pop-bride outfit to wear, with a veil ,and taken to an Italian restaurant, then to a 1970s 80s bar in town, they all had a brilliant night, returning home a little worse for wear. Anita and Mark tried to spend as much time as possible with Tracy and Elli before the wedding; it was so great to see them.

A couple of days later, Mark received a phone call saying that Pops had passed away. Mark was devastated and contemplated cancelling the wedding and honeymoon which was days away. Mark spoke to his mum and she told Mark to go ahead with the wedding and that she would put the funeral on hold until they arrived back from their honeymoon, which comforted Mark.

Chapter 18
What else can go wrong?

The day before the wedding, the guests were turning up and booking into the hotel, Anita's dad arrived with Aunt Molly, Uncle Pete and Uncle Terry; it was great to see them all. That night all the guests were in the hotel bar, Dean was spending the night at home with Mark, also with Scotty and his new girlfriend as he and Tina had unfortunately split up. Twiggy and Lisa, another of Mark's good friends were also staying at the hotel, along with old friends from their teenage years and now. Mark came and said hello to all the guests and had a couple of drinks with them before returning home with Dean. The twins had not turned up so Anita was two bridesmaids down and had a spare room booked and paid for, so Christina and Lee had the spare room with the children, so that it didn't go to waste.

That night when Anita went to bed in the hotel room, two of the granddaughters stayed in her room. Anita couldn't sleep with excitement, she rang Mark. 'Hello my sexy man, I love you, I cannot wait till tomorrow,' she said.

'I love you so much, I cannot wait either, goodnight my baby, we need to try get some sleep,' said Mark.

The morning of the wedding Anita was so excited, she went to her hairdresser's who she always used near Diane's house. Wendy, the hairdresser, was a lovely lady; she curled and arranged Anita's hair just perfect and wouldn't let Anita pay for it as a wedding present, she also gave Anita and Mark a present on top of it. The bridesmaids were at another hairdresser's getting their hair put up. When all done, Anita was now back at the hotel to get ready with the bridesmaids and flower girls. Christina, Susie and Belle had picked up the flowers and lunch for them all. Whilst getting ready, some of the guests were popping in and out of the room, cousins, Bex and Mo, Frankie, Twiggy and Lisa also. Brother Tom was helping as he was giving Anita away.

Mark rang Anita saying 'Love you my wife to be.'

'Love you too,' said Anita.

Then he told Anita that the horse and carriage would not able to get through on the promenade as gay pride was on the pier having a confrontation with the British National Party and that there were police everywhere and part of the promenade had been shut off, so it meant that she would have to get in a taxi at short notice.

When ready Anita and the bridesmaids were waiting for the taxi, she went to go out of the hotel to get in the taxi someone else jumped in it, so the receptionist rang another taxi, by the time it arrived Anita was already ten minutes late for the wedding and was starting to panic, thinking the registrar would not wait and she would not be able to marry Mark today after all. As the taxi arrived at the chapel on the promenade, Anita jumped out and ran across the tram tracks, skidding, and just managed not to fall over in her wedding dress, holding on to her veil, as it was so windy and raining. The registrar greeted Anita with a smile and told her not to panic, went through a few things with her, and calmed her down. Anita was now re-composed and ready.

The registrar put on the music CD Christina had given her, playing Endless Love as Anita walked down the aisle, thinking this is it I'm marrying the man I've loved all my life and I am so happy. The bridesmaids and flower girls were walking in front, and Christina was carrying the baby page boy as he was too little to walk. Anita looked up at Mark. Mark was smiling and kissed Anita as she stood by him and held her hand. As they said their vows they could not look at each other through giggling like teenagers. Finally they had done it, they were husband and wife. They posed for the photographer before going back to the hotel for the reception. It was a brilliant day even though it rained it did not spoil the day. It was so nice for Anita and Mark to have all their friends and family with them on their special day. They posed once again for the photographer getting groups of friends like Kim and Matt, Louise and Dan in, Fiona and Lea, Marty and Anthony in separate photos with them. Then they sneaked off to their room for a while to consummate their marriage. They then returned to the reception. Mark's mum was putting on a brave face considering she had lost Pops this week and did well to hold her composure together. The next morning, Anita and Mark went for breakfast, with all the other guests, in the restaurant, pretty much all of them were their wedding guests, so they had another chance to talk to them all before the guests left. The next day they set off to the airport heading for Turkey.

As they arrived in Turkey it was so hot and their transfer was very late, finally they arrived at their hotel, hours later than expected and were shown to a beautiful bridal suite with champagne on ice and a fruit basket. As it was late, they stayed in their room and drank the champagne and snuggled up in the big comfy bed with the air conditioning on. In the morning they woke up to beautiful sea views and went down to the restaurant for breakfast. The food was wonderful and the staff were very friendly. After breakfast they went looking around the hotel complex and found the pool with the bar in it, so decided to go in the pool and

relax for the day. They got talking to another English couple Emmy and Andy; they were only in their early twenties and a lovely couple, they ended up playing cards with them that evening. The next day they bumped into the rep, so asked him about excursions and booked 3 excursions while he was there. The first one being the following day. So they did not have too much of a late evening that day, to get up early for breakfast and go quad biking. The rep came to pick them up punctual, arriving at the centre, Anita did not want to drive one herself so shared Mark's and sat on the back, hugging Mark all the way round. They drove for miles around and stopped at the beach for lunch before heading back to the hotel with Anita getting a bruised bottom from flying up in the air on the back of the quad bike which was so much fun. That evening they met up with Emmy and Andy again and played cards with them while the entertainment was on. Anita noticed a lady sitting by herself reading a kindle; she was dressed in lilac and was wearing lilac rimmed glasses. The following day Anita and Mark decided to chill out at the pool bar for the day and sunbathe, they dipped in and out of the pool all day as it was so hot. Anita noticed the lady who was dressed in lilac from the day before, dressed in lilac again, but a different outfit. Anita decided to nickname her the lilac lady. Anita went to the bar and the lilac lady was there, Anita said hello to the lilac lady and they got chatting, the lilac lady was Scottish and had decided to have a break away on her own and relax, she joined Anita and Mark for lunch that day. Again that evening, Anita and Mark played cards with Emmy and Andy and had a good laugh with them.

They decided to go to the markets the following day, they pre-arranged transport to take them to his family restaurant which was right by the markets. Anita and Mark bought loads at the market. Mark enjoyed bartering with the traders. Emmy and Andy brought a few bits also, then they all got the free bus back to the hotel.

When they arrived back at the hotel, another couple had arrived who they hadn't seen before, they had a child with them. Then the mum shouted out to the child with a broad scouse accent, the mother looked anorexic, the man got talking to Mark. He was from London and had moved up north to be with his girlfriend who was the mother of the child. She appeared to love herself, why Anita could not think why, she just appeared common and foul mouthed. They also met a gay couple, who the waiters were trying to chat up, maybe thinking that their luck was in with two women. They were called Dani and Chell, they were a good laugh. The rep appeared again and saw all the British people sitting together and came and told them that the England match was on at his family restaurant the following evening and could he book a table for them all.

The next evening, at the rep's family restaurant were the guests, watching the match and having dinner there.

It got very noisy and the scouse, that Anita nicknamed the tramp, and her child. The lady, was very loud and put her hands on Mark and tried to undo his shirt buttons. Mark moved away from her immediately. Anita wanted to slap the tramp but wouldn't lower herself. Mark put his arm around Anita and let the tramp know that he loved his wife straight away. Returning back to the hotel, the tramp and her boyfriend were arguing and she said she wanted to hold Mark's hand as she was nearly falling over. Mark ignored the tramp and held on tighter to Anita. Other than the tramp it had been a great evening.

The next day, Anita and Mark were off for a boat trip and were picked up after breakfast. It was great on the boat, lunch and drinks were laid on for them and they sunbathed on the deck and had a stop at a secluded beach so they could relax or have a swim

before returning to the hotel. That evening they played cards again with Emmy and Andy and had a good evening.

The following day they had a mountain safari excursion booked. As they arrived at the pickup point after breakfast, the lady and the tramp were there with the boyfriend. Oh great, thought Anita, this will be such fun today not. They just happened to be in their jeep too, which was quite funny as the guides gave them water bottles to squirt at all the other groups they passed on the mountain safari. Mark just happened to soak the tramp a few times, to Anita's amusement. They stopped halfway up the mountain for lunch and drinks that had been laid on for them all and it turned out to be a brilliant day, very wet, but brilliant. When they arrived back at the hotel, Anita and Mark showered and had a nap before going down to the restaurant for dinner. After dinner they played cards with Emmy and Andy again. The next morning they decided to go for a Turkish bath, Emmy and Andy went too. It was very relaxing and a good massage with it. When they got back to the hotel it was dinner time, so Anita and Mark went to the restaurant with Emmy and Andy. The rest of the honeymoon they chilled out at the pool bar and relaxed, the honeymoon was soon over and it was time to return as husband and wife.